FROZEN GO

A Treatise on Early Klondike
Mining Technology, Methods and History

by
John A. Gould

PICTORIAL HISTORIES PUBLISHING COMPANY, INC.

L.C. CONTROL NUMBER 2001 130052
ISBN NUMBER 1–57510–082–7

First Printing 2001
Printed in Canada

Typography and layout by Jan Taylor
on Macintosh utilizing:
Aldus PageMaker 6.5
Adobe Photoshop 5.0

Cover graphics by
Mike Egeler, Egeler Designs

PICTORIAL HISTORIES PUBLISHING COMPANY, INC.
713 South Third West, Missoula, Montana 59801
(406) 549-8488   phpc@montana.com
website: www.pictorialhistoriespublishing.com

PREFACE

The story of gold, of its recovery and its use, is full of romance and goes back to the earliest human records. Egyptians and Sumerians, Romans, Greeks and "barbarians" all treasured the metal and learned how to work it into objects of beauty and great value. Gold inspired tales which have been told for centuries, of the fabulous wealth of King Croesus, of Midas' fatal "golden touch" and of the voyage by Jason and the Argonauts in search of the Golden Fleece.

Whether Jason was in fact a historical character is not known, but there certainly were Greeks who sailed into the Black Sea (Colchis) to rob gold camps there. The gold was in alluvial deposits and was separated from its surroundings by sheep fleeces set in swift flowing rivers. This was an early example of "placer" mining, of digging gold–bearing sands or gravel, mixing them with water, then pouring the mixture over skins into which the heavy gold settled while the lighter sands floated off with the water.

Throughout history, placer mining has been the most common gold mining method, although lode mining was not unknown to the ancients. It was placer mining in Saxony and on the Iberian peninsula that supplied a large part of medieval Europe's gold supply, and it was placer mining, painstakingly undertaken over centuries, that built up the treasures of Meso–America and the Andean regions looted by the Spaniards in the sixteenth century.[1]

Except for small deposits mined in the Appalachian regions of Georgia and the Carolinas in the early nineteenth century, little gold was produced in North America until the California Gold Rush of 1849. This discovery, in conjunction with the Australian Gold Rush, which began in 1851, transformed world history.

California was not an isolated gold–producing region; it was soon joined by other areas throughout the Cordillera. In the late 1850s and early 1860s, placer deposits were discovered to the north along the Fraser River and in the Caribou district. Inevitably, prospectors and miners (who were not always the same person), schooled in one of the many gold rushes that followed California, worked their way north into the Yukon River basin.

Bar mining began on the Lewes and Salmon rivers in 1881 and 1882 and on the Stewart River soon after.[2] By 1886 coarse gold had been discovered in the Fortymile area, drawing miners away from the Stewart River bars. This was followed by further discoveries in the Sixtymile River area then in 1896 by the Klondike which began the biggest northern rush of all.

DEDICATION

This manuscript is dedicated to my father, Robert S. (Bob) Gould, who came to the Klondike from Nova Scotia in 1901. He staked claims on Nugget hill, Hunker creek in 1903, which he worked for the next 55 years and are still being worked by his grandson Peter. It was from him and other old time miners that I got much of the information used in this manuscript.

John A. Gould
Author

INTRODUCTION

Although concerned primarily with placer gold mining technology in the north, this book will begin with a brief discussion of the importance of gold in human history and will indicate the geographical and historical factors that made the development of the Yukon gold mining industry possible.

THE PROSPECTOR

Early mining in the north depended upon primitive methods and equipment, which possessed the double advantages of being inexpensive and of proven effectiveness. How these methods were used and, more importantly, how the various methods were adapted to the special problems of the north will be discussed in some detail. In addition to these natural problems, those of logistics, of expenses and of government regulations had also to be dealt with. The many difficulties that the early sourdough miners faced in their struggle to extract gold from the frozen north will be described.

It was not until the richest deposits were exhausted that it became necessary to consolidate claims so that more efficient mechanical methods could be used. Besides hand mining, this book will cover such methods as open cut, self-dumping and hydraulic mining. Dredging, however, will only be mentioned in relation to thawing. The thawing of the permanently frozen deposits was a process developed in the north to meet the unique problems of northern mining. A section will discuss the different methods used and the experiments that led to the eventual use of cold water to thaw large blocks of ground for dredging purposes.

The material in this book comes from the resources in Dawson City as well as references gathered over the years. Much comes from the personal experiences of the principal author, his father and many old timers, based on many years of placer mining.

TABLE OF CONTENTS

Photo Credits

J.A. Gould – Author
KNHS – Klondike National Historic Site
PHPC – Pictorial Histories Publishing Co.
UW – University of Washington, Special Collections
YCGC – Yukon Consolidated Gold Company
YA – Yukon Archives

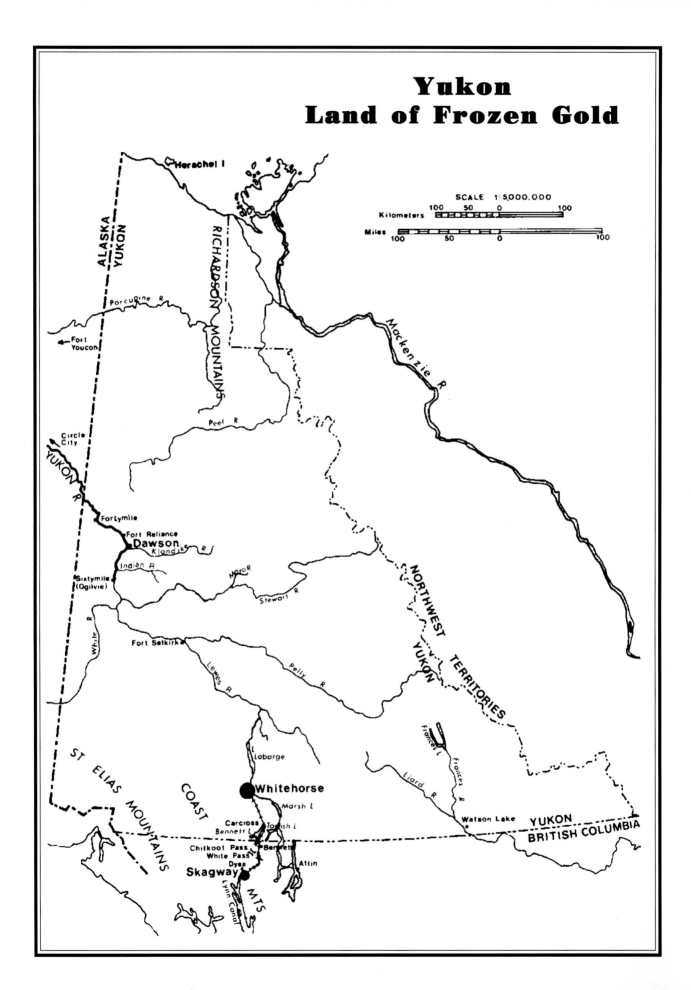

Yukon
Land of Frozen Gold

THE SETTING

The Importance of Gold

Gold is a dense, bright element which combines three important properties. First, it is chemically inert, so it is virtually indestructible. The gold found in Tutankhamen's tomb in the 20th century had been deposited there over 3,000 years earlier, but it had lost none of its lustre. Gold is also extremely soft and easy to work. It can serve as jewelry or as coinage; it can be used industrially; or it can be stored in ingots. None of these uses is final, and it can be easily recycled as new needs arise. Thus the world's total store of gold constantly increases, as new supplies complement, but do not supplant, old. However—and this is the most important reason for its importance—these supplies are limited. Gold is found in minute quantities, and its volumes are measured in ounces or grams. There has never been enough gold to meet the needs set for it, so it has always had a unique scarcity value. Exact figures are obviously lacking, but it has been estimated that of the 801,000 metric tons of gold produced up to the early 1970s, only some 10,000 were produced before Columbus' discovery of America, some 30,000 M.T. between 1500 and 1900 and the rest in the present century.[2] The "needs" set for gold have been constant throughout history. It serves as a medium of exchange, a standard of value, a store of wealth and as a thing of beauty. Which is most important is irrelevant; all are intertwined.

Although there have been "moneyless" societies in history, and many others which used such diverse items as iron, cowrie shells or huge rocks as media of exchange, gold has been central to western civilization. The only mineral comparable to it is silver. These two minerals were also important in the ancient world, in Egypt, Greece, Persia and the Roman Empire, all of which possessed monetary systems based upon gold and/or silver. Gold was sought as loot; it was also mined in placer deposits and lode mines in places as diverse as Nubia, the Black Sea basin and the Iberian Peninsula.

Gold was scarce during the Middle Ages of European history with most of Europe's supplies coming from placer deposits in Iberia (e.g. the River Tagus in Portugal), Germany ("Rhinegeld"), and lode mines in Saxony and Austria. Some also came from "Guinea" in West Africa, but this gold passed through many hands before reaching Europe.

Medieval Europe was poor but self–contained. After the Crusades, it began to reach out in trade to western Asia and northern Africa. It was no coincidence that the first gold coins minted in Europe since Roman times were struck in Italy in the thirteenth century. Europe had little to offer its richer neighbors; it could only pay for its imports in the two universally accepted media of exchange—gold and silver.

The scale of gold mining increased by the later Middle Ages, particularly in the Hapsburg domains in Germany and Spain. There was not enough produced, however, to meet the commercial needs of Europeans, much less pay for imports. New sources were needed and were sought by Iberians who, being the furthest from eastern sources of supply, were liable to pay the highest prices, and who had the advantage of highly developed mining traditions. In the mid–15th century, the Portuguese travelled south to the Guinea coast of West Africa in order to reach the source of supply there. By the end of the century the Spanish had gone west, in search of the gold of Japan.

Both succeeded, and in the process, set in motion the domination of the world by Europe. The Portuguese acquired their Guinea gold in trade, the Spanish their American gold and silver in pillage. The gold famine in Europe changed rapidly to a glut. Spain squandered its wealth, losing its capacity to feed, clothe, house or defend itself to its poorer, but more dynamic, northern neighbors. In order to maintain itself, after skimming off the treasures of the Aztecs and the Incas, it developed extensive lode and placer mining deposits in Mexico, Peru and Columbia. In the 18th century, the Portuguese in Brazil discovered vast gold deposits, so that from the 16th until the 19th century, Latin America consistently produced most of the world's gold.

The expansion of gold supplies in Europe from the beginning of the 16th century meant a gradual inflation of prices. This destroyed the productive capacities of Spain and Portugal, which had been able to purchase anything they needed. It stimulated production in England, France and Holland and laid the basis for their power and wealth. Increasing supplies of gold made credit easier and investments safer, enabling Europe to reverse its earlier inferior relationship with Asia and to initiate the Industrial Revolution by the end of the 18th century.

The Industrial Revolution meant a dramatic expansion in trade and production, but contemporary banking and financial institutions were unable to cope with this expansion. Wealth was still measured in silver or gold bullion, but the relationship of silver to gold was not known. While debts incurred in gold could be paid off in gold, they could also be settled in silver. In the latter case, there was the possibility that adequate payment could be avoided. Similarly, banking institutions could issue notes, but the value of these notes was variable, and their effects often inflationary. There was also a serious problem in the 18th century (reversed in the 19th) of the drain of specie to India and China. This appeared to deplete Western coffers and threatened to impoverish Europe again. Finally, the violent upheavals associated with the French Revolution and the destruction of the Spanish Empire in America initially interrupted, then decreased dramatically, the shipment of bullion from Latin America to Europe.

To resolve these problems, the British government decreed in 1821 that the amount of paper money issued depended upon the size of Britain's gold reserves, and that gold was to be freely convertible. The result was the establishment of a fixed value for the British pound—the Gold Standard—making the pound literally "as good as gold" and therefore a firm foundation for both internal and external commerce.

The gold standard was effective in underpinning commerce with a stable financial base, but it could not increase gold production. This caused something of a paradox: production and trade expanded as the effects of industrialization reached out from Great Britain, but consumption was constrained by the limited supply of gold. Legislation could determine the value of gold, but it could not determine its production.

By the 1840s, the economic growth that was such an integral part of industrialization was slowing down. In spite of increased productivity and the development of new industrial techniques, the gold standard threatened to end the experiment that the Industrial Revolution represented. Two solutions to the problem were possible: stimulate consumption by abandoning the gold standard and encouraging inflation or increase the amount of money by bringing more gold supplies into production.

The first was unthinkable; the second happened with the California and Australian gold rushes of the 1850s. These initiated a half century of "poor men's" gold rushes that culminated in the Yukon in 1896. First California, then other parts of the American West such as Nevada, Colorado, and the Dakotas, British Columbia in Canada and finally the far north were prospected and where gold was found, were mined. During this period, the technologies and the mining codes developed in California out of the needs of new mining communities were extended and modified to meet local needs elsewhere. Huge areas were opened up to hard rock mining, agriculture, forestry and industry by miners, and these areas were quickly integrated into North American society. Placer gold deposits were catalysts, attracting labor and capital into new districts. Some were "high graded," then degenerated into ghost towns; others became prosperous communities on the basis of mining or other activities. Dawson and the Klondike fields initially appeared likely to go the latter route. In the end they went the former, but not before making important contributions to Canada and to the history of mining technology.

The Geology of the Klondike Gold Fields

In exceedingly minute quantities, gold is distributed throughout the world, on land and in the sea, but in such small amounts that its recovery costs far exceed the value of the metal extracted. Of greater significance are those few areas of the earth where gold ore has been concentrated, by the shifting of the earth or by the action of water, into quantities which can be extracted economically.

What can be extracted economically varies according to two factors—technology and price. In the former case, deposits along a stream can be mined cheaply and efficiently by one man equipped with no more than a shovel and a gold pan. More difficult to extract is gold located in quartz, which must cover the cost of crushing the ore before profitability can be achieved. Similarly, alluvial deposits locked in frozen gravel demand more sophisticated technology to meet the higher costs of production. Finally, the minute deposits dispersed throughout the Pre–Cambrian formations of South Africa are impossible to extract except by the use of both highly sophisticated technology and chemistry. Profitability in the case of free nuggets can be achieved at almost any price, but it took increased prices, as well as technological efficiency, to transform dispersed, or smaller, quantities of ore into auriferous deposits.

Gold prices were determined by markets and gold supplies by geology. Knowledge of practical geology and the ability to distinguish auriferous zones marked the successful prospector. Some features of the Klondike gold fields applied to all gold–bearing zones;[4] others were particular to it, presenting both unique opportunities and challenges to northern miners.

It was important first of all to recognize that there was no "motherlode," no one huge body of gold ore whence alluvial deposits originated and the discovery of which would bring great wealth; nor was gold deposited entirely in a random manner. It was, for example, more often associated with rugged terrain comprising igneous deposits than sedimentary regions or ancient, eroded hills. It was likely to be found in acidic rock such as silica, granite or quartz, containing silicon dioxide which "trapped" mineralization. Gold locked in quartz veins was termed "lode" and had to be extracted by crushing, but "alluvial" deposits were those which had already separated from the quartz as it decomposed and which were moved by the action of water.

The greater part of Klondike gold was detrital in origin and derived from auriferous quartz veins cutting older schists, especially the igneous schist of the Klondike Series.[5] Besides that derived from broken quartz veins, a small amount was precipitated from water carrying gold in solution. The Klondike goldfields comprise some 800 square miles, bounded by the Yukon River to the west, the Klondike River on the north, Dominion Creek on the east, and the Indian River to the south (see Map 1 on page 4). This is a deeply trenched area, thoroughly dissected by a number of small streams tributary to the main river. With the uplifting of much of the area between the Alaska boundary and the Stewart River, the Klondike River and a number of its tributaries cut deep channels in the high level gravels.[6] In this manner, some of the gold in the high level gravels was reconcentrated in the present day valleys of Bonanza, Eldorado, Hunker, Dominion and other creeks.

The geological factors of the auriferous regions of the Yukon basin—rugged terrain, igneous rock formations, swift flowing streams—were general to much the Cordillera, but two geographical factors were unique. The first was aridity caused by the rain shadow cast by the Coast Range; the second was the long, cold winter of northern latitudes. Because the central Yukon receives little precipitation, it escaped the scouring glaciation of the Ice Ages. The minute deposits of gold laid down from decomposing quartz and concentrated by moving water remained within the basin of their origin. Elsewhere water dispersed gold deposits; here

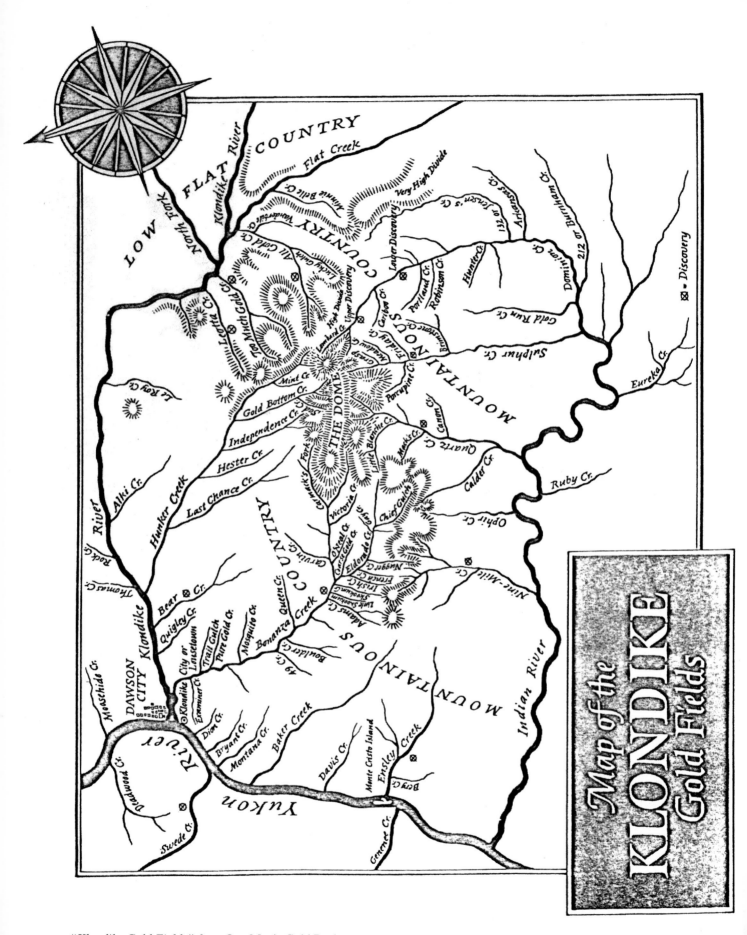

"Klondike Gold Fields" from One Man's Gold Rush.

cold prevented dispersal, allowing ice to lock it into permafrost as effectively as if in quartz.

In the Yukon and in Alaska, gold is found concentrated close to or in bedrock, more so than in other placer mining fields. This is due mainly to the clean character of the "wash." There is so little clay in most of the wash that it has not hindered the descent of gold through the gravels to bedrock. This clean character helps the modern bulldozer miner; in most cases his sluice box is less than 40 feet long, and 80% of his cleanup is in the first ten feet of his sluice. Most of the gold falls out of the gravels almost as soon as the water hits it.

Auriferous gravels in the Klondike area can be classified as follows:

1. Low level gravels
    1.a. Creek gravels: These are alluvial deposits situated in the beds of the valleys. These gravels are detritus in origin and range from a few feet to over 100 feet in thickness. They rest on bed rock and are composed of frozen muck, decomposed matter, bones (including those of extinct mammals) and moss.
    1.b. Gulch gravels: These are located in the upper portions of the main creek valleys, differing from creek gravels only in being coarser and more angular.

1.c. Bar gravels: These are the accumulations of gravel in river beds which are covered at high water and exposed at low. These are composed of washed gravel in which the auriferous zones seldom exceed 25 feet in depths, more often extending no more than two or three feet.

2. Intermediate (terrace) gravels: These occur at various points in the deep slopes of the present valleys, and are simply the remnants of former valley bottoms. Gravel here is similar to creek gravels, although it is usually more eroded.

3. High level gravels:
    3.a. River gravels: These are ancient creek deposits, overlaid near the mouths of some valleys by gravels put down by the Klondike River when it ran at a much higher level. These can be up to 175 feet thick.
    3.b. White channel gravels: These are ancient creek deposits laid down in wide, flat valleys which characterized the district before the last general rise in the level of the region. They now occur in wide benches some 150-300 feet above the present valleys. Their distribution is irregular, as is their size, varying in width from 100 feet to half a mile, and in thickness from three or four feet to 150.[7]

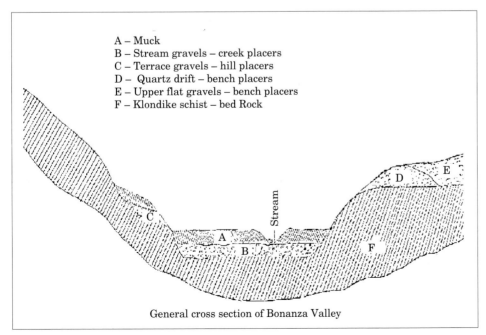

A – Muck
B – Stream gravels – creek placers
C – Terrace gravels – hill placers
D – Quartz drift – bench placers
E – Upper flat gravels – bench placers
F – Klondike schist – bed Rock

Stream

General cross section of Bonanza Valley

Figure 1: From Preliminary Report of Klondike Gold Fields.

A typical cross section of a valley in the Klondike gold fields is shown on page five. It shows the different levels of gravel deposits.

The bedrock in the streams of the Klondike is covered with a layer of gravel from one to four feet thick; this gravel and about two feet of the bedrock contain gold. The formation from this pay gravel to the surface varies to some extent on the different creeks, but is generally composed of layers of muck, sand and gravel (figure 2 below).

Gold is found in the stream gravel everywhere, but in paying quantities only along portions of the valleys and portions of the hills and benches; no fixed rule can be formulated as to where the gold is or why it is there.

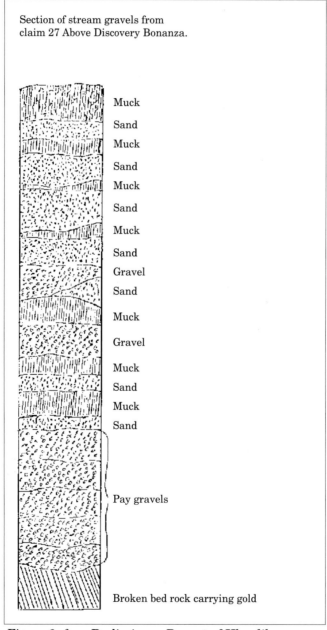

Section of stream gravels from claim 27 Above Discovery Bonanza.

Muck
Sand
Muck
Sand
Muck
Sand
Muck
Sand
Gravel
Sand
Muck
Gravel
Muck
Sand
Muck
Sand

Pay gravels

Broken bed rock carrying gold

Figure 2: from Preliminary Report of Klondike Gold Fields.

Discovery

The rival claims of Robert Henderson and George Carmack for the title of discoverer of the Klondike gold fields in 1896 are recounted below,[8] but it is worth noting that the rich placer deposits of the Klondike Valley had been tested and found wanting a decade earlier.

In 1895 a report was made to the Yukon Order of Pioneers by Peter Nelson, that a party of four—Joe Ladue, Don Sprague, John and Peter Nelson—had done some prospecting on the Klondike River in 1886. They had gone overland from Fort Reliance, located about ten miles below the mouth of the Klondike on the Yukon, struck the Klondike about 40 miles up and prospected on the way downstream. This report stated in part:

On our first day of travel down the Klondike we stopped on a bar on the left side of the river, in the late afternoon. The bar had a heavy growth of willows and was composed of coarse wash. Prospecting it, we found it would go 25 to 30 cents to the pan for about 3 inches below the surface. We did not consider it would pay us to stop as we could made $50 to $100 a day on Stewart River during low water. [9]

With the discovery of gold at Sutter's Mill in California in 1849 and the ensuing gold rush, it was inevitable that prospectors and those looking for their own pots of gold would work their way north. Gold was discovered in Oregon, in Idaho, and later in the 1850s in British Columbia. The resulting influx of people opened up new country, but the hardiest prospectors continued to push into the unmapped regions of the far north.

The Yukon and Alaska were the last areas they reached, having been preceded by Russian and British explorers and fur traders. Sir John Franklin's party visited Herschel Island in 1825 while exploring the Arctic coast west of the Mackenzie delta. The first permanent penetration of the Yukon by whites did not begin until the early 1840s when Hudson's Bay Company's Factor Robert Campbell ascended the Liard river and crossed the divide to a westerly flowing river he named the Pelly. In 1843, he went down this river to a larger one which he called the Lewes. As a result of his efforts, the Hudson's Bay Company built two posts in this northwest corner of America, Fort "Youcon" (Yukon) at the confluence of the Porcupine and Yukon rivers, and Fort Selkirk where the Pelly flowed into the Lewes. In 1850, Campbell made a trip down river from Fort Selkirk to Fort Yukon, passing the mouth of the Klondike and proving that the Lewes and the Yukon were in fact the same river.

The Hudson's Bay Company operated trading posts in the Yukon basin for furs, not for gold. A letter home from one of its employees at Fort Yukon in 1864 provides an indication of the company's priorities.

There is a small river not far from here that the minister, the Rev. McDonald, saw so much gold on a year to two ago that he could have gathered it with a spoon, I have often wished to go, but can never find the time. Should I find gold in paying quantities I may turn gold digger, but this is merely a last resort when I can do no better. [10]

Not surprisingly, the company did little to encourage the search for gold, and it was only in 1872 that serious prospectors arrived in the country. In September, Arthur Harper and five others set out for the Yukon, met another party consisting of L.N. (Jack) McQuesten, Alfred Mayo and James McKnipp on the way, and traveled up the Mackenzie and Porcupine rivers to Fort Yukon, arriving in July 1873.

It was impossible for them to survive on prospecting alone, so they combined prospecting with fur trading. In 1874 Jack McQusten set up a trading post at Fort Reliance, 12 miles down stream from the mouth of the Klondike. Over the next 20 years, these and other prospectors who came over the Chilkoot Pass or up the Yukon River alternately trapped and prospected, the former providing them with sufficient capital needed to undertake the latter. Communications improved, so more prospectors arrived every year, some to winter over, others to spend the summers in the north and then return to the outside. Gold prospects there were in abundance, but no major strikes until 1885 when sufficient gold was found on the bars of the Stewart River to keep over 100 men busy. In 1886 coarse gold was found on the Fortymile River, causing a rush to that area and the establishment of the town of Fortymile at the mouth of the river of the same name,

In 1894 Robert Henderson from Nova Scotia arrived in the country with a small party. They prospected along the bars of the Upper Yukon and rocked out about $54 in fine gold at the mouth of the Pelly River. When they reached Joseph Ladue's trading post at Ogilvie, he told them of the latest finds in the country. After a short stay, Henderson headed for Indian River, and he prospected along Indian River as far as Quartz Creek; stories of Henderson's activities differ at this point. It has been said that Henderson, along with a man named Collins, worked for a season on Quartz Creek for William Readford who had been mining there since 1894. Not satisfied working for someone else, in 1896 Henderson crossed over the divide at the head of Quartz Creek to a creek he called Gold Bottom, where he found what he thought was a good prospect.[11] Later that summer, he made a trip to Ogilvie Post for supplies. While there he told Joe Ladue, the owner, of his prospect on Gold Bottom and suggested Ladue move his post and sawmill closer to what might become a new gold field.

On his return trip, knowing that the Indian River would be very low and hard to ascend at that time of the year and reasoning that Gold Bottom flowed into a creek he called All Gold (Hunker), he met Geo. W. Carmack, his Indian wife Kate and two Indian companions—Skookum Jim and Tagish Charlie. He told Carmack of his find on Gold Bottom and invited him over to see for himself and to stake a claim.

A few days later Carmack did make a trip to Gold Bottom, but he was not impressed with what Henderson had located. On his return trip to the mouth of the Klondike, he and his companions traveled over the hill and down Rabbit Creek. In the late afternoon of August 16, 1896,[13]

while preparing camp for the night, the party found gold on a bedrock outcrop. Carmack was able to fill a cartridge case after panning twice, and the next morning he staked two claims as the discoverer. His companions staked on either side of Carmack's claims. At the same time they renamed the creek "Bonanza."[14] They then headed for their camp on the Klondike. It is worth noting that Carmack had promised Henderson that if he found anything on Rabbit Creek he would send a message back to Henderson, but he forgot to do so. From their camp, he and his companions went to Fortymile, where they recorded their claims. When Carmack showed his coarse gold to the miners there, they recognized that it had not come from the Fortymile area. Having heard of Henderson's find on Gold Bottom, they rightly assumed that Carmack had made a find—so the Klondike Gold Rush was started.

It was only in July 1897 that the "outside" world became aware of the fabulous gold discovery that had been made in Canada's remote northern region. Rumors of gold had been trickling outside for several years, but it was not until the steamer *Portland* landed in Seattle on July 17, 1897, with a half ton of gold (the steamer *Excelsior* had landed in San Francisco a couple of days earlier with a like amount of gold) that the outside world really became aware that there was gold in the far north, apparently in large quantities. This was a shot in the arm to North America, which was deep in a depression that had started several years earlier. A hundred thousand people from all walks of life dropped what they were doing, acquired outfits and headed for this fabulous gold find. Little did they realize that the 3,500 miners scattered throughout Alaska and the Yukon district had already heard about it and were on site, staking the majority of the claims. Few of those who set out actually reached Dawson.

Originally, those who came north during the gold rush came to get rich quickly and go back home to a more comfortable life. Once they arrived on the scene however, and found all the claims staked, many of them went to work for wages. Others sold their outfits for what they could get and headed home. Many reverted to their old trades and professions, making new lives for themselves in the Yukon.

METHODS

Prospecting

Prospector
Who wants the treasures rare, Gold nuggets small and big,
Must search with hope and ne'er despair, Then dig and dig and dig.
Author Unknown

It was the early prospector, always in search of the pot of gold, working his way north from the southern gold fields of California and British Columbia, who contributed most to opening up the north country.

The early prospector was not secretive about his finds; whenever he stopped at a trading post, he told the trader of his prospects, information that would be passed on to others. It was in this way that interest was created in the Klondike area. Several men were looking for Bob Henderson's find when Carmack made his discovery August 16, 1896.

Prospectors had been working in the Yukon region since the late 1870s, but mining can scarcely be said to have begun until some years later, and then at first, on a very small scale. Bar mining began on the Lewes and Salmon rivers in 1881 and 1882, and the first successful strike was made on the Stewart in 1885.

The early prospector in the north had no geological information to help him; he went at it on the basis of instinct and practical experience, using his pick, shovel and gold pan, sampling the river and creek gravel bars wherever he had

the opportunity. If he found a little fine gold, he would move on upstream, checking whether the amount in the pan increased and got coarser; if so, he knew he was getting near the source of a bigger deposit.

When the prospector found what he considered a decent prospect on the surface, he could sink a shaft to look for better pay, knowing that the best gold deposits were usually near or on bedrock. The first thing a prospector did was to clear an area of the insulating layer of moss and brush to the size of the shaft that would be sunk, usually three feet by five feet. Once bedrock was reached—and if the pay was a little better on bedrock than on the surface—he then drifted a short distance in the direction of the dip or slant of the bedrock, looking for good pay. If none was found, the prospector could sink other shafts nearby, perhaps across the valley a short distance. He could do this until he found the pay streak or determined that there was nothing there. If he found a five–cent–to–the–pan prospect, he could make "wages;" if he got as much as 25 cents to the pan, then he had good ground (see Figure 3 below).

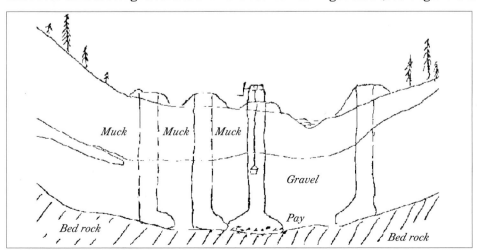

Figure 3: from Klondike Stampede, *showing how to cross cut a creek when prospecting.*

In the *Klondike News* of April 1, 1898, an article was published for the first–time prospector entitled "How to Prospect."

HOW TO PROSPECT

A prospector should be able to recognize gold, mica, galina, and chalcopyrite.

He should familiarize himself with the gold–bearing rocks of the district he expects to prospect.

He certainly should be able to pick out granite, sandstone, limestone, slate, serpentine, and schist as well as talc, trop, deorite, diabase, dolerite, dolomite, and porphyry. But if one knows nothing and hardly that about prospecting, and cannot tell serpentine from salmon eggs, it is no reason why one should not try, but if this is the case it will be better to confine oneself to some known gold belt. The usual method of the Yukon prospector is to confine oneself to the bed of a stream and look for high rim rock along its banks.

That is where one can see the bedrock projecting from the hillside. Colors of gold, however small in the gravel on the rimrock, are enough to warrant sinking a hole.

The first thing is to get through the muck (decomposed vegetable matter), which is found on all northern streams. This varies in depth from two to forty feet....

Pure muck can be removed with pick and shovel at the rate of four or five feet per day, but if mixed with sand, must be thawed. When the top gravel is reached put in a "fire" and pan as you go down. Remember that the very richest claims only yield five or ten cents to the pan in the top gravel. If the gravel removed from

the "hole" is good, it should be placed on a bed of moss, which is called the "dump bed."

Upon reaching bed rock, a good miner goes down two or three feet deeper and drifts down stream. The chamber thus formed is afterwards filled up with waste and refuse of the mine, so that any water coming in will run into the lower chamber and not put out the fire.

A poorly constructed fire, however, may thaw out the "roof" and cause much trouble, so a few words as to "how to put in a fire" will not be amiss. Place shavings and fine kindling along the lower face of the drift and build up with short dry wood. Then put on the green wood left unburned from the day before. On top of this the greenest wood obtainable should be closely piled to force the heat against the face of the drift. This is called "blanketing," and the top layer of wood is stood on end to the height of the paystreak. This fire is left to burn all night, or until burned out, and the gravel thawed by its heat is removed at once. Great care must be taken to avoid foul air and gas, as many deaths have occured from carelessness in this regard.

If your candle goes out when descending into the shaft come up at once. Many claims have an air shaft and there are numerous inventions in the way of pumps and fans that will clear away danger. The old timer generally agitated the air in his shaft by waving a blanket over the Mouth.[15]

The end of the trail.

Once mining started, most miners continued to take prospect samples of the ground to make sure they were still in good pay. The early miners would also sample their dumps to keep a running account of the day's production. Four times a day, five pans of gravel would be taken from the dump, one from each side and one from the top. The results of these 20 pans would be consolidated, and then the value would be reduced by 50 percent; this figure was used along with the amount of gravel mined to give an estimate of the day's gold production.[16]

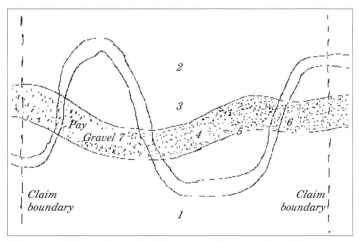

Figure 4: Plan of creek claim showing paystreak in relation to creek and also prospect holes.

Once dredging started, it became necessary to find new ways to prospect the ground, especially in the Klondike Valley where the ground was thawed and there was a lot of water, making it very hard to sink shafts. It was in support of dredging that the Keystone placer drill came into full use in the Klondike. In 1906, the Canadian Klondike Mining Company had four of them prospecting the valley.[17]

The drill used had a six–inch chisel–type bit to cut down through the gravel (photograph 1). In thawed ground, casing would be driven ahead of the drill to keep the hole at a uniform size. Using a formula, the driller knew how much yardage he drilled for any depth of ground, so values taken from the drill hole in gold could then be computed into values per cubic yard. The dredging companies drilled a line of holes 50-100 feet apart across each claim. This told them the width of the pay gravels and the yardage of dredgeable ground, as well as the depth and type of gravel deposit.

Once dredging started, prospecting or sampling would continue. Each dredge had a panner on the dredge; it was his job to take samples from the buckets and pan them, especially as they got down to what was considered the bottom of the pay gravels. When the bottom of the paying gravels was reached, the panner signalled the winch man who raised the bucket line, moved the dredge ahead to a new position, and started a new digging session.

Keystone placer prospecting drill in operation. The drill hole has just been bailed out, and the man is panning the material that was in the bailer.
1906 *KEYSTONE CATALOGUE*

Costs

The hand–mining phase of the Klondike era lasted only about three years, until 1899, by which time the rich ground had been exhausted. What was left could not sustain the expenses of hand mining, which necessitated the importation of machinery to move larger amounts of gravel. However, in order to use the larger machines—steam shovels, dredges, etc.—it was necessary to consolidate claims into larger blocks.

It is difficult to determine the exact cost of hand mining during this brief period, but what information there is available—wages paid and the amount of gravel one man could move with a shovel in a specific period of time—indicates that it was expensive. For example, it is known that wages as high as $1.50 an hour were paid for labor, and that over a ten–hour day a man could shovel up to six cubic yards into a sluice box, or wash four cubic yards with a rocker. Thus a cubic yard of gravel had to have at least $2.50 worth of gold in it to be sluiced to pay for labor, before meeting other costs. With hand mining, it was impossible to reduce costs below $2 a cubic yard, and in many cases, the basic cost was as high as $5 a cubic yard.

By 1899, when a larger labor force comprising the thousands of men attracted by the rush had reduced labor costs to 40 cents an hour, other costs, such as room and board at $5.50 a day and the government's 10% royalty on the gross output of all mines, ensured that costs would remain high. In a statement to the government in December of 1897, Alexander "Big Alex" McDonald listed the cost of many items: labor, $1.50 an hour; $2 an hour for skilled workers for a ten–hour day. Lumber was 40 cents a board foot, delivered. Riffles were $25 a set with an average of 72 sets per claim. Wheelbarrows were $5 each, shovels $3.50 each. Cord–wood was $25 a cord delivered to the claim. The cost of building a 12 by 14–foot log cabin was $600. Freight rates were very high at 25–30 cents a pound from Dawson to Grand Forks, a distance of 12 miles. In the winter, this dropped to ten cents a pound. McDonald estimated that it cost $5 to handle a cubic yard of dirt.[18]

In 1899 a miner named John McGillivray estimated what certain commodities would add to the cost of mining a claim of 2,000 square yards.[19] Two years earlier, a miner paid a half to one ounce of gold for an axe and $1.50 to one of his laborers to go to town to get it. At a cost of $20, this axe added one cent a yard to his cost. An installed window for the miner's cabin cost $120, a tin wash basin $3.50 and lumber delivered to claims on Eldorado up to $700 for 1,000 feet. This increased costs $1.40 a yard, demanding very rich pay. In 1899 costs were not much less, although there were fewer claims than there had been in 1897 able to bear such huge costs. Things were made worse when the government took out millions in royalties and taxes, without reinvesting in the Yukon to decrease costs. A wagon road from Dawson to Grand Forks would, in McGillivray's estimation, have cost $75,000 to build and would have reduced freight rates to three cents a pound. In fact, rates were not less than eight cents a pound, adding $500,000 to the cost of shipping 5,000 tons to Grand Forks. Summer rates of 25 cents would mean $2.5 million added on to the cost of getting freight to Dawson.

Harold Innis stated that winter drift mining cost $10 per cubic yard, but open–cut mining during the summer months could be done for only $5 a cubic yard.[20] One reason was that thawing by the summer sun meant a saving of $2.50 per yard, and that a man could shovel half again as much gravel six cubic yards in the summer and only four cubic yards in the winter, in a ten–hour day.

In June 1909, the cost of sinking a shaft eight feet by eight feet and 55 feet deep was $9.96 a foot, for a total of $548.23. Labor was $400; six cords of timber at $8 per cord was $48; the cost of dressing timber was $50; and it was $50 for the steam to thaw the ground.[21] The cost of sinking a smaller shaft (three by five), of the size that would be used by a one or two–man operation, was about the same as the larger shaft; considering the volume of dirt removed, the cost was approximately $2.50 per foot of depth.[22] The cost of drifting or tunnelling in a four–foot by three–foot drift was also $2.50 a foot. The cost of sinking a shaft varied according to the size of the shaft, but the cost of moving the dirt per cubic foot did not vary much—14 to 16.5 cents. Sinking a shaft four–foot by six–foot to 30 feet was $3.11 per foot; a four–foot by five–foot shaft was $2.80 per foot; and a six–foot by six–foot shaft was $4.40 per foot.[23]

Another cost in early mining was for the "laymen." Some of the claim owners preferred to let others work their ground on a lease, or "lay," as it was called. The claim owner got 50% of the gross output, and the layman got 50%, but out of his 50%, he had to pay all the expenses of mining the ground. One operation on a 50% lay used a self–dump with a large bucket, and a 42–man crew handled 300–cubic yards in a 24–hour period. Sluicing would start in early May and run for 140 days. In this time, the crew would handle 421,000 cubic yards, averaging $3 per cubic yard for a gross output of $126,000. Fifty percent, or $63,000, went to the claim owner; operating costs were estimated at $1 per cubic yard, or $42,000, leaving $211,000 for the operator.[24]

T.A. Rickard cited a case where six men shovelling in 15-20 cubic yards in ten hours, at 1898 wages of $1.50 an hour, cost $4.50 a yard. This meant that the pay gravels had to produce well over $4.50 per cubic yard for every cubic yard moved in order for the claim owner to make some money.

Some of the early claims did produce gold in such quantities that many men became rich. One operator had eight men shovelling for three ten–hour shifts, and then cleaned up his sluice, recovering $45,000 or $275 a cubic yard—$187,50 for every man hour worked.[25]

Listed at right is the equipment needed for a typical self–dump operation in 1909.[26]

In some cases water was a cost. If the mining was done on the hillsides or benches above the creek, then it had to be pumped. Some enterprising operators set up pumping stations and then charged the miners for the water. According to C.W. Purington, miners bought water for a ten–hour period, paying 15 cents per miners inch.[27] A sluice head of water, 50 miners inches, would cost $7.50 a day. After several attempts to pump water, it was soon determined that it was cheaper to bring it by force of gravity, no matter how far it had to come.

Besides paying for pumped water, there was also a fee to the government if you acquired your own water. The fees were: $10 for 60 M.I. or less; $25 for 60-200 M.I.; $50 for over 200 M.I. This licence was good for five years. The water regulations also laid down how the water should be measured:

1. One miners inch (M.I.) = 1.5 cubic feet of water per minute.
2. When measured through a rectangular orifice, one miners inch shall mean 1/12 (one twelfth) of the quantity which will discharge through an orifice 6 inches wide by 2 inches high made of 2–inch planking planed and made smooth. The water shall have a constant head of 6.25 inches above the center of the orifice. It was determined that an opening 6 inches wide by 2 inches high with a head of 6.25 inches would deliver 11.99 miners inches of water per minute (130 gallons per minute).[28]

A.H. Day constructed a long flume from claim 216 Below Discovery to 273 Below Discovery on Dominion (5.75 miles long) and sold water under pressure to the miners for $1.25 a sluice head—his was by the hour.[29] In some cases, where water was scarce, the charge would be as high as $8 per sluice head.

40 H.P. Scotch marine waterback boiler,return flues	$1,300
15 H.P. horizontal engine	375
6 H.P. Gould centrifugal pump with foot valve	300
10 H.P. hoisting engine	450
200 feet 3/4–inch cable	38
500 feet 3/8–inch cable	50
20 1/2–inch thawing points 8 feet long	200
4 wheelbarrow buckets	60
10 pan American wheelbarrows	100
100 feet 5/8–inch steam hose	65
1 dozen silver dollar shovels	18
200 feet 3/4–inch pipe	24
Miscellaneous tools and equipment	125
Total	**$3,105**

One writer gave the following as the cost of mining 20,000 cubic yards from a 30–foot deep shaft and a pay–streak that was four and a half–feet thick.[30]

1 shaft 30 feet long	$130
Timbering shaft and part of tunnel	170
112 cords of wood at $10	1,120
Labor – 10 men	3,696
Cost of deadwork and upkeep	1,534
Total	$6,650
Number of operating days	56
Daily Capacity (cubic yards)	60
Cost per cubic yard	$2

This put the gravels in a dump ready to wash; the cost of washing was another 60 cents to $1 per cubic yard.

Once dredging started, a larger volume of gravel would be handled; as a result, costs again went down, but it was not until the 1920s, when cold water thawing was perfected, that costs fell to the point where gravels that had less than 25 cents in gold for each cubic yard of gravel could be handled profitably. The Yukon Consolidated Gold Corporation records show that in the early 1920s, the company thawed 490,834 cubic yards of gravel with steam at an average cost of 24.74 cents per cubic yard. From 1924 to 1934, it thawed 14,024,568 cubic yards with cold water at an average cost of 5.06 cents per cubic yard.[31] Their No. 3 dredge in the Klondike Valley was able to dig ground at a cost of only 4.69 cents per cubic yard. At this rate a recovery of only 9.64 cents per cubic yard was profitable. This big dredge averaged about 12,000 cubic yards in a 24 hour day. Its No. 1 dredge on Dominion Creek cost 23.29 cents per cubic yard, but the recovery was an average of 52.54 cents per cubic yard; these figures are for the years 1935 to 1941 inclusive.

The cost of recording a claim has long been $10, with a renewal fee of $10 a year on or before the anniversary of the date it was staked. It is also necessary to do or have done a certain amount of work per year for each claim held; in the case of a placer claim, it is $200 per claim per year. The Yukon Placer Mining Act (1906) set out a schedule of fees that can be used in determining the value of the work performed. A claim owner could renew his claim for up to five years providing sufficient work had been done and a $50 fee was paid.

15

Regulations

When the first prospectors came into the Yukon basin, there were no regulations to greet them, and they saw little need to establish any. Gradually, however, as their numbers increased, disputes arose that demanded resolution, and it became obvious to distant governments that there were paying quantities of gold in the Yukon to be taxed, regulations were developed or imposed.

Throughout history, monarchs have controlled, or at least monitored closely, the mining of gold.[32] Because the minting of coinage was a sovereign's prerogative, the mines from which the gold was extracted were considered to be the property of the sovereign. They were worked by the miner who paid a percentage of the output—royalty—to him. It could be as high as half of the gold extracted, but such exactions did little to stimulate production. Consequently, regulations had to be modified in order to encourage prospecting and mining by allowing the miner to keep the fruits of his labour, turning over to the ruler a smaller proportion of a vastly increased output.

By the late Middle Ages, four important principles had been established to regulate mining: mineral ownership was separate from surface rights; only the sovereign could grant the right to work mines; the sovereign maintained part proprietorship in the mines; and the miners appointed and controlled management.[33] It was under these laws that the Spaniards mined in the New World, gradually modifying existing Spanish laws to the reality of local conditions (e.g. how to determine a claim, what constituted abandonment). The result of this in 1783 was the first mining code, the *Ordenanza de Mineria*, which, while modified, remained suited to Klondike conditions a century later.[34] The code determined that claims would be square, with corners marked by permanent monuments; that the miner paying a fee to the Crown had unrestricted access to the minerals of the claim; and that a certain amount of work had to be done each year in order to retain title. The Spanish tax was the *quinto*, initially a "fifth part of all

metallic production of the Indies, without deduction for expenses…paid to the royal treasury."[35] In practice, the *quinto* amounted to nowhere near 20% of the output; by the end of the 18th century it was down to a figure closer to five percent.

California was in transition from Mexican to American rule when gold was discovered there in 1848, so neither Mexican law (based upon the Spanish *Ordenanza*) nor American common law provided a basis for California mining regulation. What emerged from California combined features of Mexican law, the experience of European (e.g. Cornish and Saxon) gold seekers, and practical experience. The most important feature of the California mining regulations was that they were not imposed by a sovereign but drawn up by the miners themselves, assembled in "miners' meetings." They eliminated the concept of a royalty paid to a sovereign, preferring rather the notion of a fee paid to a mining recorder (representing the community) in order to fix a claim. The meetings determined such matters as the size of claims, the markings, the amount of work necessary to maintain a claim, and methods for determining if a claim were abandoned. Size was variable, depending upon richness and difficulty and ranging from ten square feet to 100. More important than size, however, were the restriction to one claim, the right of title granted to the first locator, and the necessity for continuity of work to maintain ownership. These regulations protected the interest of individual, small–scale miners from speculators or corporations.[36] Neither the California nor the United States governments regarded miners as trespassers, so neither demanded acknowledgment of sovereignty in the form of licences or royalties or imposed rules. Gradually the rules of different mining camps grew similar, as the best features were broadcast and the worst abandoned.

In 1866 the United States government codified what western practice had established into a national mining law, then modified it slightly in 1872. One feature of the 1872 law was to increase the size of placer claims to 20 acres, much larger than originally determined in California. When American miners arrived in the north, they maintained both the tradition of the miners' meeting as the basic unit of government and the large (1,320 by 66 feet) 20–acre claim which extended "from rim rock to rim rock."[37]

Miners schooled in California helped open up the Australian and British Columbia gold fields. In both of these British dominions, their miners' meetings were denied the rights they had exercised in the United States, but the good sense they demonstrated was usually accepted. Thus in British Columbia, the miners established the size of claims—and this was put into law by Sir James Douglas—but they purchased annual licenses for their claims and saw the gold laws administered by a Gold Commissioner.[38] Similarly in Australia, placer miners were considered to be trespassers on Crown land until they obtained a license. This, in effect, acknowledged the sovereignty of the Crown, after which they were able to work in peace, backed by the full force of the law.

Initially Yukon mining regulations were based upon the miners' experiences, which meant the 1872 American mining code. By the late 1880s, Canada had asserted sovereignty but had no mining regulations for the practical administration of Yukon mining. As William Ogilvie, then surveying the international boundary, politely phrased it, "The mining regulation were in a very embryonic state," being based upon British Columbia laws.[39] These provided for placer claims limited to 100 square feet, which was felt to be far too small for Yukon conditions, particularly as American laws allowed vastly larger claims. The miners urged, and Ogilvie agreed, that creek claims be at least 300 feet long along the valley and from "base to base of the hills on either side" in width.[40] Other problems relating to royalties and the merits of miners' meetings as compared to Department of the Interior regulations were also raised but not immediately resolved. What was evident was that the combination of American mining codes and their interpretation on the basis of local circumstances, as was the practice in Alaska, was more favorably regarded by the miners than the vague and inappropriate Canadian regulations.

It was only in 1896, on the eve of the gold rush, that the frequent miners' petitions finally resulted in modified Canadian regulations. These allowed for 500–foot creek claims (the rest remained 100 square feet) and limited each miner to one claim—except for the discoverer in each new field who was allowed a second adjoining claim. Methods of staking were simplified, and the minimum age for making a claim was lowered from 21 to 18. Upon payment of $15 to the Gold Commissioner, the miner could begin work. He had to put in three months on the claim to retain ownership of it.[41] The system was still not as favourably regarded by the miners as was the American, but at least it was organized in a code.

When George Carmack staked his discovery claims on Bonanza Creek the morning of August 17, 1896, he was entitled to two claims—Discovery and No. 1 Below, both 500 feet long. No. 2 Below was staked for one of his companions, No. 1 Above for the other. Soon the rest of the creek and others in the district were also staked, but in the absence of both competent government officials and adequate legal machinery, staking and recording of claims was done inexpertly by miners. This necessitated constant resurveying and reallocation of ground. William Ogilvie was called upon to regularize the situation. This he did, in spite of massive obstacles, to the evident satisfaction of the miners.

In the spring of 1897, word of the richness of the Klondike gold strike reached Ottawa. The existing regulations were inadequate, and the legal machinery for enforcing these regulations hopelessly so. The Canadian government had nothing in its experience to assist it in framing new regulations. Those it did provide were based on the assumption that the mines would soon be worked out, and the government set out to extract maximum revenue in the shortest possible time.[42]

An *Order in Council, No. 1189*, dated May 1, 1897, reduced the size of the creek claims to 100 feet along the general course of the stream and to the base of the hill on either side; or, if the latter was less than 100 feet, then the full 100 feet was allotted, making the minimum size of a claim 100 feet square. This same *Order in Council* set out the nature and size of all claims. A "bar–digging" claim was a strip of land 100 feet wide at high water, and then extending into the river to the lowest water level. A "discovery" claim was to be 200 feet in length; a "bench" claim, 100 feet square with a post at each of its four corners. Only every other claim could be staked—the other alternate claim was reserved for the Crown, to be sold later at a public auction. A fee of $15 was charged for the first year, and $10 per year thereafter, once a claim had been granted. A claim could not be left unworked for more than 72 hours except in case of sickness, or if a leave of absence had been granted by the Commissioner. The claim grant did not give the miner surface rights or rights to the timber on the claim, nor could he stop anyone from crossing his claim.[43]

These mining regulations were totally unacceptable to the miners who protested against both their provisions and the inept (if not corrupt) method of their implementation. The federal government responded to the protests in January 1898 with a modification of the earlier *Order in Council* which increased the size of the claims to 250 feet along the general direction of a creek or stream, and the side boundaries were to be where the base of the hill rose three feet above the general level of the creek, but no more than 1,000 feet, and no less than 100 feet, on each side of the base line. A hill claim was to be 250 feet along the general direction of the adjacent creek and thence to the summit of the hill, with a maximum of 1,000 feet. Other placer claims were to be 250 feet square. All claims had to be as near rectangular in shape as possible, marked by two legal posts. At this time, the government also changed the stipulation that each alternate claim was reserved for the government—every alternate ten claims were

now reserved. For example, when a discovery was staked, the next nine claims could be staked, the next block of ten was reserved for the government, the following ten could be staked, and so on. The size of the discovery claim was increased to the original size it had been in 1896— 500 feet long, or two discoverers could stake one such claim each to a total of 1,000 feet. It would now cost $10 to obtain a "Free Miner's Licence" to perform any work in connection with mining, $15 to record a claim and $15 to renew the claim each year. The government had imposed a royalty of 20% in 1897, on the gross (i.e. before costs were met) output of all mines producing over $500 a day, and 10% on all claims producing less than that. In an area like the Yukon, especially under gold rush conditions, this constituted virtual expropriation. There was thus every incentive for miners to evade payment of royalties, which the administration hoped to overcome by reducing the royalty to 10% and limiting its application to gold produced over $5,000 a year. [44] This was later reduced to five percent in 1901, and abolished in favor of a two and one half percent "export tax" in 1902.

There were constant opportunities for lawsuits, as regulations were maladministered or changed, and huge profits could be made or lost between staking and cleanup. "Poolhall" mining—which demanded no knowledge of actual mining conditions—encouraged speculation and litigation. The problems were serious, but as the cartoon below from the *Klondike Nugget* shows, they did not always have to be treated seriously.

From the November 18, 1899, Klondike Nugget.

IN THE ABSENCE OF REGULAR SCHOOL SUPPLIES THE NUGGET SUGGESTS

Another type of mining claim, and one which was a potent source for legal wrangles, was the hydraulic concession encompassing large blocks of land. The first such claim granted was the Anderson Concession, Hydraulic Reserve No. 1—it took in two and a half miles of ground on the lower end of Hunker Creek and was granted in September 1897. The largest concession was the Boyle Concession, Hydraulic Reserve No. 18, taking in 40 square miles of the Klondike Valley from the mouth of Bonanza to the mouth of Hunker Creek and from ridge on either side of the valley. It was granted in November 1900.

These concessions were a continual bone of contention for the miners. No one was allowed to stake claims within the concessions. The miners attempted for years to get them cancelled; the newspapers were after the government to have them cancelled; and a number of court cases were held whenever someone tried to stake a claim. [45] The concessions were slowly done away with until the big dredging company Yukon Consolidated Gold Corporation ceased operations in 1966. There were then only two left—the Anderson Concession and the Boyle Concession. These eventually ceased to exist, finally opening up ground to the modern miner.

Only in August 1906, with the passing of the *Yukon Placer Mining Act,* was a system of mining regulations created which was based upon Yukon conditions and which reflected the wishes of Yukon miners. The need for a consolidated code had been obvious from the time of the gold rush, but it was swept up into Yukon political disputes over responsible government and the granting of concessions. Only in 1906, by which time the Yukon appeared to have escaped the fate of so many ephemeral mining camps and the local council had submitted a draft mining code to Ottawa, was it passed.

A year before, the federal government had doubled the size of placer claims, reduced the fees for miners' licences, and made several changes to the mining regulations, but all by *Order in Council.*[46] These new changes were now consolidated in statute, no longer subject to the whims of ministers, nor vulnerable to special interest groups. The *Yukon Placer Act* was so satisfactory that it has remained in place, little changed, since 1906.

This act laid down the nature and size of claims, who may stake, the recording and renewal fees, and the amount of work necessary to "represent" a claim in a year. It also allowed for the grouping of claims, so that work done on any one claim could be used to represent a number of claims. Placer claims on a creek were to be 500 feet long and 1,000 feet each side of the base line. Hill and bench claims were to be 500 feet along the general direction of the adjacent creek and 1,000 feet back. A discovery claim, to one locator, was to be 1,500 feet along the creek, and to two locators, a 1,000 foot claim each.

Once a claim was staked, it was necessary to do a certain amount of work per claim each year to be able to renew the grant. The value of the work done was not its actual cost, but was determined by a schedule set down by the government, and varied depending on how the work was done.

This schedule of allowable costs was:

Shaft	Sinking
First 10 feet of depth	$2 per foot
Second 10 feet of depth	4 per foot
Third 10 feet of depth	6 per foot
Fourth 10 feet of depth	8 per foot
Below 40 feet	10 per foot

cont.

This schedule of allowable costs, continued:

Tunnelling
a) in unfrozen ground

first 25 feet	$2 per foot
beyond 25 feet	3 per foot

b) in frozen ground

first 25 feet	3 per foot
beyond 25 feet	4 per foot

Drifting from Shaft

a) in unfrozen ground	$2 per running foot
b) in frozen ground	3 per running foot

There shall be, in addition, one dollar per running foot for every 10 feet in depth of the shaft from which the drift is running. In measuring the drift, each running foot shall be made for such additional work on a basis of each running foot having a width of 4 feet.

Timbering

In shaft	$3 per running foot
In drift	2 per running foot

Open Cutting

a) Ground sluicing	$0.50 /cubic yard removed
b) Stripping by scraper	0.75 /cubic yard removed
c) Hand shovelling	1.75 /cubic yard removed

Drilling
In all cases, both in steam and hand drilling, the actual cost of such work.

Hydraulicking, Dredging and Steam Shovelling $0.50 per cubic yard

The use of water for mining purposes was regulated by the government. A water right was applied for at the mining recorder's office; notices had to be posted in the office, at the point where the water was picked up, and at the point where it was used. The fee was based on the number of miners inches applied for: $10 up to 60 inches, $25 for 60 to 200 inches, $50 over 200 inches. [47]

Dimensions of Orifice in Inches		Head in Inches	Miners Inches Per Minute	Cubic Feet Per Minute
Width	Depth			
6	2	6.25	11.99	17.98
12	2	6.25	24.25	36.38
18	2	6.25	36.39	54.59
24	2	6.25	48.70	73.05
4	4	6.25	15.71	23.56
6	4	6.25	23.57	35.35
12	4	6.25	47.30	70.95
18	4	6.25	71.65	107.48
25.5	4	6.25	101.58	152.37

Materials

A land of harsh climatic and geological extremes, the Yukon provided little off which the professional gold hunter could live. He had to bring most of his food supplies and all of his mining equipment with him, for he could trust to the land for little more than fuel and such fish, meat and vegetables as he could take time from prospecting to find.

The early miner or prospector probably brought only what he needed, relying on the trading posts to supply him with many of the heavier and bulkier items. Whether he brought the items from the "outside" or got them from the trading posts "inside," there were some items he probably brought with him. If he came by way of St. Michael and up river by steamer, he would have been able to bring considerably more than if he came in over the Chilkoot or one of the other passes, where he would have had to carry everything to the headwaters of the Yukon, build a boat or raft and float down river.

In order to enter the Yukon at the time of the gold rush the cheechako prospector had to bring sufficient supplies for a year. Lists of necessary supplies were prepared, based on 20–years' experience in the Yukon, which purported to provide the newcomer with all he needed. The price of such goods was high outside, but it was substantially higher inside—if the goods could be obtained there.[48] One example of an Edmonton–based list was:

GROCERY LIST

400	lbs. flour	$10.00		25	lbs. hard tack	2.00
150	lbs. bacon	16.50		1	lb. citric acid	.90
100	lbs. navy beans	4.50		8	lbs. compressed vegetables	3.25
40	lbs. rolled oats	1.40		1	lb. pepper	.25
20	lbs. corn meal	.75		1/2	lb. mustard	.25
10	lbs. rice	.75		1/4	lb. evaporated vinegar	.75
25	lbs. g. sugar	1.63		75	lbs. evaporated fruits	10.00
10	lbs. tea	4.00		20	lbs. candles	3.20
20	lbs. coffee	8.00		6	tins 4 oz. extract beef	3.00
2	doz. condensed milk	4.50		4	pkg. yeast cakes	.40
10	lbs. baking powder	5.00		1	pkg. tin matches	.75
2	lbs. baking soda	.20		1/2	lb. ground ginger	.20
20	lbs. salt	.40		6	lbs. laundry soap	.37
20	lbs. evaporated potatoes	5.00		6	cakes borax or tar soap	.50
5	lbs. evaporated onions	2.50		2	bottles Jamaica ginger	.50
					TOTAL	**$91.45**

HARDWARE

1	camp cook stove	$7.00		1	galvanized water bucket	.40
1	fry pan	.25		2	granite plates	.30
1	coffee pot	.75		1	knife, fork and spoon	.25
2	granite cups	.30		1	butcher knife	.25
1	bake pan	.75		1	axe and handle	1.00
1	set nested kettles	2.40		1	small hand axe	.60
						cont.

1	whet stone	.10	15	lbs. assorted nails	.75
1	hammer	.50	1	drifting pick and handle	1.25
1	brace and bits	1.25	1	long handle shovel	1.00
1	pair gold scales	2.00	1	gold pan	.75
1	38.55 Winchester carbine	16.00	200	ft. 3/8 inch rope	1.20
100	cartridges	3.25	5	lbs. oakum	.60
1	7 x 7 heavy duck tent	4.50	10	lbs. pitch	1.00
1	jack plane	.90	2	caulking irons	.60
1	inch framing chisel	.25	1	pair goggles	.15
1	whip saw, 6 feet	7.50	1	compass	1.00
1	hand saw	1.00	1	quartz glass	.60
2	files	.25	1	lb. quick silver	.90
1	draw knife	.75	**Total**		**$62.30**

(This hardware list includes all that would be required if the party consisted of five or more).

Several items not indicated on the outside list were also necessary, such as:

1 sledge hammer (4-8 lbs)	1 ruler, or tape measure
1 carpenter's level	1 gold poke

Once he found a place to mine, he would need a rocker, long tom or sluice box (see below); these items he would make on site from lumber he either bought from a mill (if there was one nearby) or whipsawed from nearby trees.

To travel during the winter months, he would need a toboggan or hand sleigh which could be used for hauling supplies or wood to his camp. Picks were sharpened by heating them in a fire and then pounding them to a point on an anvil. An anvil was too heavy to cart around, however, so a large boulder was used; in fact, the first blacksmith shop in the country used a large boulder. [49]

Much of the equipment used for hand mining was also needed for mining with machinery. The rocker or long tom might not have been necessary, but in many cases they were used to assist with the cleanup. The whipsaw gave way to a sawmill or the purchase of lumber from a commercial mill.

EQUIPMENT LIST

Boilers	Tubular	Locomotive Scotch Marine Horizontal return	Pumps	Piston Centrifugal Pulsometer Chinese Water wheel
	Upright PipeBoilers	Thimble Porcupine		
Winches		Single drum Double drum	Self–dump carriers	The Dawson Carrier
Scrapers	Horse–drawn slushers Steam–powered		Self–dump buckets	
Steam points			Hose and couplings	
			Pipe and fittings	

Boilers

A variety of styles and size of boilers were used in the Klondike gold fields. If used only for thawing ground, a small one of 1 1/2–horse power was large enough for a one or two–man operation; it probably would have been a pipe boiler and could have been carried by two men.

Most self–dump operations used a boiler of approximately 35–horse power, as would scraper operations. A self–dump or scraper operation was likely to have more than one boiler, depending on the size of the operation—one to power the self–dump or scraper, one for any pumps being used, and possibly a small one for thawing.

An operation using large boilers for power would need large quantities of wood. If the men cut and hauled their own wood, a team of horses and sleighs would be necessary, as well as a buzz saw powered by a small steam engine to cut wood into appropriate lengths for the boilers. If the wood was supplied by a contractor, then the miner would need only the buzz saw.

Other pieces of equipment needed were sluice boxes, riffles, and a blacksmith shop with all the necessary tools. Needs for this equipment depended on the size of the operation. Some basic items were:

Forge	Cold chisels
Anvil	Files
Hammers – several	Drills – with bits
Hardies – several	Saws – hack & hand
Coal or charcoal for forge	

If the operation had horses, then it would be necessary to have a few farrier tools—so the horse could be shod—as well as some harness repair equipment.

Type of Boilers

Scotch Marine: this type of boiler, designed to power deep sea ships, was used quite extensively in the Klondike and came in a variety of sizes.

This pipe boiler as constructed of heavy duty water pipe. The housing of sheet metal stands next to it.
KNHS

Locomotive: this, as the name implies, was like the steam engine of a train. Many of these were used in the big dredging operations to produce the steam required on the dredge and for thawing ground ahead of the dredge. They were also used on board the steam boats.

Here a pipe boiler supplies power to a steam engine which is turning a centrifugal pump, pumping water into a high flume that transports it to the mining operation.
YA, GILLIS COLLECTION

Horizontal Return Tubular: there were a few larger units in use, ones that had fire boxes built of brick work. The one used to power "Big Alex" Mc-Donald's pump on Hunker was an example of this.

N.C. Company's stationary–type boiler, Dawson water front, used for heating Front Street buildings. Larger than McDonald's Hunker boiler.
KNHS

Pipe Boilers: there were three kinds: pipe boiler, porcupine boiler and thimble boiler, or cross tube boiler as it was sometimes called. Pipe boilers came in a variety of sizes, from small portable ones of 1 1/2–horse power that could be carried by two men to large ones four feet square by eight feet high. Porcupine boilers had a large inner water tube with short, small pipes radiating out from the sides, much like the quills of a porcupine. These small pipes were closed off on the outer end. Thimble boilers were just the opposite: the water jacket was around the outside, and short pieces of pipe projected from the inside of the water jacket inwards into the head source.

Opposite: In the near photo, the remains of a large pipe boiler show the piping used. The large pipe is the steam dome. The far photo shows the pipes in a porcupine boiler. This is a part of a large boiler, probably the heat exchanger.
BOTH KNHS

Upright Tubular: several sizes of this kind were used, and they were the fire tube kind—that is, the heat rose up through tubes, heating the water that surrounded the tubes.

Left: This type of boiler, used in many of the early mining operations, was very easy to move; all the accessories would be taken off and the boiler laid down and rolled to a nearby new site.
KNHS

Above: This "dog house" boiler was portable and used for prospecting and other small jobs.
KNHS

Buckets

The hand–powered windlass style, of 1 1/2–cubic foot capacity, was made of wood, with rope handles.

Self–dump buckets, made of metal, had approximately ten cubic foot capacity.

Windlass bucket of 1 1/2– cubic foot capacity.

Metal self–dump windlass bucket.
KNHS

Not all operations used buckets; some used platforms with three sides. These would hold four to six wheelbarrow loads of gravel. The platform would be hoisted by steam and guided by a rope, and the man handling the rope to guide it would also pull on the rope to dump it at the right time.

Steam is used here to hoist a platform with three sides. One man holds a guide rope which is probably used to dump the pay gravels into the sluice. The platforms are loaded with wheelbarrows, and horses and scrapers are used for clearing the tailing and also for stripping off the overburden.
J.A. GOULD

Riffles

Most of the early miners used poles or wooden blocks, and in some cases rocks, for riffles. Later on, when the hydraulic and dredging operations started, angle iron Hungarian– style riffles and iron–shod, two–inch lumber were used.

This style of riffle was known as the Hungarian riffle. These are covered with rubber, and many were covered with iron. They were used in an undercurrent where only fine sand and gravel ran over them.
KNHS

Other Items Used by Early Miners

Hand Windlass Bucket: there are a number of these around. Their size was 18 inches by 18 inches at the top, 14 inches by 14 inch at the bottom, and ten inches deep holding seven or eight pans of gravel, or about 1–1/2 cubic feet.

Homemade cart: these were used to haul the windlass bucket along the tunnel to the bottom of the shaft along pole rails.

Windlass bucket resting on a homemade cart which ran on pole rails to transport ore gravel from working face to bottom of shaft where it was hoisted.
DAWSON MUSEUM COLLECTION

Homemade cart used to haul windlass bucket along adrift or tunnel to the bottom of the shaft. The rollers underneath are notched to roll along pole rails.
DAWSON MUSEUM COLLECTION

Homemade mine car: these were built of lumber, using heavy barn door hinges and iron rods. This example is located on Gold Bottom Creek.[51] There are no wheels on it, and there is no information regarding the type of wheels it used: were they of the mines car style, using railroad type rails, or were they the type of wheels that used poles for rails?

Remains of a homemade mine car. A large hinge on the bottom allowed it to be dumped. It may have had iron wheels and light mine car tracks or poles for tracks.
DAWSON MUSEUM COLLECTION

Hand pump: an old one was found on Hunker Creek, at Jack Fraser's and A. Close's mining operation. Squarely built, it looks similar in style to the kitchen pumps of years ago. It was probably used for supplying domestic water. [52]

Homemade hand pump. The small rod through the top was pulled up and pumped water, either for domestic use or to pump water out of a working area.
DAWSON MUSEUM COLLECTION

Chinese pump: this was powered by an overshot water wheel, and used mainly to keep water from the working area. [53]

Water wheel: these were usually used by bar miners to bring water to their operation. A large water wheel set in the river had buckets or cans attached to it in such a way that as the river current turned the wheel, the buckets were filled and eventually dumped into a flume which carried water to the operation.

Wheelbarrows: there were two sizes and two styles of wheelbarrows: with ten–inch (the more common) or with 15–inch pans, and they could be side or end dump. Most were metal pan wheelbarrows with wooden frames and iron

wheels, but, there were some that were all metal, using iron tubes or pipe for a frame. There were also some that had wooden pans.

Fifteen–pan capacity side–dump wheelbarrow—a favorite. KNHS

Water Supply

Water plays so important a role in placer mining that without a good supply, all activity comes to a standstill. In fact, it is so essential that during the summer of 1906, a rainmaker from California was hired under contract to make rain in the Yukon. The summer of 1905 was so dry that many of the mines shut down due to lack of water. In July of that year there were several forest fires raging within sight of Dawson. John T. Lithgow, comptroller for the Territorial Government, proposed to the Yukon council that a contract be entered into with Charles M. Hatfield, a rain maker who purportedly had had considerable success in California. As it turned out, he was too busy in California that year to come north. During the next winter, a contract was make with him to come to the Klondike in June of 1906. The contract was for $10,000, $5,000 put up by the government and $5,000 by the miners.[54]

Hatfield arrived on June 6, along with his gear and his brother who was his assistant. By June 22 he was set up on King Solomon Dome at the head of Hunker, Quartz, Sulphur, Monimion and Bonanza creeks. The *Yukon World* reported every day or so—in large headlines—on what Hatfield was doing. The *Dawson Daily News* did not consider it worth such intensive coverage and made only occasional entries on his efforts. There was some rain in June, but the miners said it was only enough for the cabbage patches. By July 4 there was no rain. The committee which had hired Hatfield held a meeting[55] and decided to give him another two weeks. On July 19 it determined to meet with him and have him explain why there was no rain: he had made no rain in July and only 1 3/4 inches of rain in June. On July 23, 1906, they went again to meet with Hatfield, but the latter never showed up, so the contract was cancelled.[56]

In the meantime, Chief Isaac of the Moosehide Indians told the *Dawson Daily News* that he had four medicine men making "big medicine," so that Hatfield would make no rain.[57]

When Hatfield's contract was cancelled, he loaded all his equipment into a buggy and was on his way to town when the rain came in a downpour. Chief Isaac claimed his medicine men had made this rain!

Hatfield was only allowed expenses from the contract and was never heard from again. There were several poems written on Hatfield's attempt to make rain. One by a C.S.W.B. appeared in the *Yukon World*, June 1906. It was entitled "Omar revised," and one verse went as follows:

Oh, thou with chemicals and stink
Arrange the rainfall so that all may drink
Thou wilt not cause disastrous floods,
  and thou
Tell us that in your system there's a kink.[58]

The average precipitation in the Klondike is 10-12 inches with about four inches of this being snow. Many miners built snow fences during the winter by piling up snow, so that the spring thaw in their area would last longer. This did not work; it just made a larger runoff.[59]

The spring runoff of melting snow each year does not last very long—two to six weeks, depending on the size of the collection area and the method used to collect the water. By 1900, after steam thawers had come into use, the size of the dumps to be washed was much larger than in the past. Mining was being carried out on the hills and benches where the water supply was nonexistent unless pumped or ditched from the creeks. The miners working on the lower end of the creeks had more water—even though it was very thick—than the miners working near the upper end of the creeks, where there was very little water, and almost none at all during a dry summer. The miners had also stripped the surrounding hills of all trees, so if it did rain, there was nothing to hold it back. The rain could last a few days, and all run off in a rush, or if the rain was heavy enough, it would cause flood conditions on some creeks.

Constructing Upper Bonanza Dam, 1908. Three of these dams were built by mining companies on Adam, French and Bonanza gulches.
YCGC

Claim #12 Eldorado looking up French Gulch, showing the fluming used to transport water back and forth along the creek. In the center of the picture can be seen flumes used to take water from the main flume to the mining.
J.A. GOULD

It was after the Gold Rush of 1898, when steam was used for thawing, that summer mining really got started. The miners on Bonanza and Eldorado creeks worked together to make the best of the available water; flumes were built on trestles carrying the water back and forth across the valley and on down the valley. The miners at each claim would take what they needed and ensure it then went back into the flume, in addition to whatever seepage or bedrock water there was, to the benefit of everyone. This allowed all the miners at least some water. Of course, it soon became very thick, even with the addition of clean water from whatever small gulches there were along the creek. Because dirty, muddy water does not wash all the gold from the gravel but carries it on out the end of the sluice box, it is worth the modern miner's while to rework the old tailings.

Not everyone prayed for rain, though. Miners on some river bars, such as those on the Stewart River, were unable to mine until late summer;there was too much water before then. They had to wait until the level of the river had dropped enough to uncover the bars, so the less rain there was, the better it was for them.

Once pumps were brought into the country, the miner was able to build sumps at the lower end of his claim and return water for sluicing. This did not give him cleaner water, but it certainly gave him more water.

The miner resorted to many methods to get water in large enough quantities to be able to wash the gold from his gravel deposits:

1. Ditches and flumes, to divert creeks or streams.
2. Dams, to store water during spring runoff.
3. Pumps
   a) Piston for pressure and pumping up to high levels; these could be either steam or electric powered.
   b) Centrifugal for pumping into sluice boxes and recirculating; also steam and electric–powered.
   c) Pulsometer pump for thawing and draining a work area; steam–powered.
   d) Chinese for draining work area; water–powered.

Although most miners moved the water to the gravel deposit, a number of operators moved the gravel to the water, or at least closer to the water, using chutes and tramways.

Ditches and Dams

Ditches, dams and flumes were used right from the start to get the water to where it was needed, but early efforts were on a small scale. Once machinery became available and corporate mining was started, a larger, more reliable supply of water was needed, especially when the hydraulics started on the bench high level gravels, some 300 feet above the valley floor.

The small tributaries of Bonanza, Eldorado and Hunker creeks had a sufficiently steep gradient for the miners on the benches to construct ditches along the hillside, at a flatter grade than the creek, and eventually reach the valley bottom and pick up what water was there. During the spring runoff, there would be plenty of water from the beginning of thawing until early June; by this time the snow was all gone, as was most of the ice formed during the winter months. The water would then dry up rapidly, unless there were rainstorms to help with the supply. If the catchment area was large enough, some of the miners would have an hour or two of water a day for sluicing, but many would end up with no water, unless there was rain. Of course the miners lower down the creeks always had some water. There were hundreds of ditches dug to supply water to the bench miners—ditches from one mile in length to 70 miles long, capable of carrying from 50 miners inches to 5,000 miners inches.

Mining on the benches required water, so attempts were made to pump water. It was soon found that it was cheaper and better to bring water by force of gravity, no matter how far it had to come.

There were at least three large dams constructed at the heads of three of the creeks around Bonanza—one at Upper Bonanza, one at French Gulch on Eldorado, and one at Adams Gulch on Bonanza. There were also a number of small reservoirs built at the various claims.

The largest of these dams was built by the Yukon Gold Company, which acquired the right

This Asahel Curtis photo shows the extensive workings on Upper Eldorado Creek, including mine dumps, water systems and miners' tents. Every inch of this creek was staked, and fabulous fortunes were made here.

to "impound the unentered and unappropriated waters of Bonanza Creek" just below Carmack Forks.[60] At a cost of between $250,000 and $300,000 it erected a dam and conduit system in 1906 to trap runoff water in the spring for use in hydraulic mining.[61] The dam was huge— 400 feet long at the bottom, 500 at the top, 230 feet wide at the bottom, tapering to 20 feet at the top. It had a catchment area of over 14 square miles creating a reservoir nearly a mile and a half long, and holding 43,500,000 cubic feet (350,000,000 gallons) of water.[62] It could provide enough water to last 40.3 days of hydraulic mining with a flow of 500 miners inches. Under normal conditions, this provided adequate water for hydraulic work all summer. The water was carried in ditches and flumes to the north side of Upper Bonanza to a point above Grand Forks, across from Gold Hill. Here

it was siphoned across Bonanza in an inverted siphon, arriving on Gold Hill with a head of 150 feet.

Another somewhat smaller dam was built on Adams Creek by the lessees of the Matson and Boyle concession at a cost of $75,000. This dam had a capacity of 6,600,000 cubic feet (58,000,000 gallons) of water and was able to supply 600 miners inches of water for hydraulic operations on the hills and benches between Adams and Boulder creeks on Bonanza.[63]

Water was essential for all placer mining operations in the Yukon, so any attempts to control it had political implications. Mineral rights did not include water or timber, which often had to be supplied to claims. If it were provided for small-scale individual miners by a publicly-owned water system, then individual miners could operate profitably. If, however, an individual or corporation could control access to water, he (or the corporation) could use it for hydraulic and dredging purposes or charge individual miners unregulated prices—in neither case benefitting small–scale operations.

One man recognized at an early date the importance of water for mining in the Klondike— A.N.C. Treadgold, an English entrepreneur.[64] He realized the labour–intensive mining methods of the gold rush could not last long and attempted to ensure that the inevitable change to capital–intensive working of the low grade gravels that remained would be on his terms. For this he needed concessions—water and mining—in order to consolidate claims and work them profitably. In 1901 he obtained a concession which gave him most of the goldfields, as well as the exclusive right to construct water systems and to take any timber required. In return for the concession, its holders would build a ditch to deliver a flow of 1,000 miners inches of water, one half of which would be available to other claim holders at a rate not to exceed $1 per M.I. per hour, up to $50 an hour to operate a four–man sluice box.

Although the federal government gave Treadgold his concession, the opposition in Dawson was intense. Gradually the "Octopus," as the concession was termed, was dismantled. At one point in early 1902, it was modified, so that the cost to miners for water dropped to $0.25 per M.I. per hour, but this was still unsatisfactory. In the 1902 election for the Yukon's first member of Parliament, J.H. Ross campaigned on a pledge to dismantle the concession and to press for a publicly owned water system. The latter was particularly important in 1902, because not only were the most easily worked claims already "high–graded," a lack of water that year had seriously impeded mining operations and forced many small–scale operators into bankruptcy. Obviously some sort of water system was needed, but whether it was to be federally funded and publicly owned (to the benefit of the small–scale miners) or privately owned and used for capital intensive hydraulic and dredge mining was not clear. In 1905 the Dominion government did send an engineer to investigate the feasibility of a publicly built and owned system. While technically feasible and certainly desirable to the miners, such a publicly owned system was not built. By 1905 po-

litical power in the territory had shifted, and any federal commitment to a publicly owned system was forgotten. With the construction of the large dams, the acquisition of water rights from gulches and other mountain streams by corporations, as well as their acquisition of large blocks of claims for hydraulicing, the government dropped the idea of a subsidized system.

In the end, the Yukon Gold Company built the ditch Treadgold had originally proposed and used all the water itself. There were entrepreneurs who did sell water to some of the miners, at $0.15 per M.I. per day. Water that would flow through an opening 175 inches by two inches with a head of six inches during a ten–hour period cost $52.50 a day, a sum attractive only on very rich claims.[65]

Two large ditches were built by the Yukon Gold Company. One went along the hillside and across the slide at the north end of Dawson to Moosehide Creek, to supply water to the Aklen Potato Patch hydraulic mine on the Klondike River, above Ogilvie Bridge. The plan was to build this ditch to the headwaters of the Twelve Mile River in the Ogilvie Mountains, but it only went as far as Moosehide Creek. Instead, the Yukon Gold Company built the Yukon Ditch, which did take water from the Twelve Mile and Tombstone rivers, but the route was different.[66] It was built in conjunction with a hydroelectric

Men construct a water diversion ditch to move water to a hydraulic operation. This particular ditch moved water from Moosehide Creek down river from Dawson, across the slide at Dawson and around to the Alkin hydraulic mine on the Klondike River upstream from the Ogilvie bridge.
YCGC

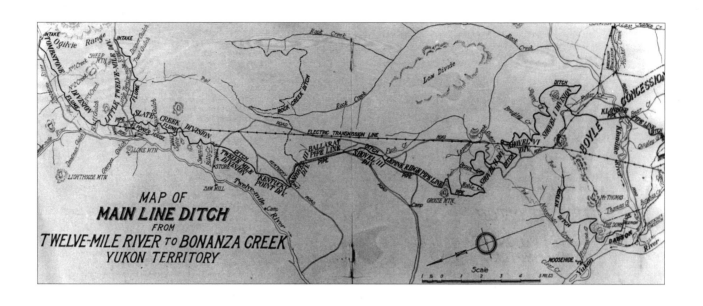

MAP OF
MAIN LINE DITCH
FROM
TWELVE-MILE RIVER TO **BONANZA CREEK**
YUKON TERRITORY

Top: Water flume of the Yukon ditch moved 5,000 miners inches of water from the Ogilvie Mountains, 70 miles away, to the hills along Bonanza Creek for hydraulic mining purposes.
YCGS POWER FLUME #2

Bottom: California redwood was used in some of the inverted syphons on the Yukon Ditch to transport water across some of the small valleys.
YCGS LEPINE PIPING #3

Inverted syphon across LePine Creek, showing wood stabe pipe in use.
YCGS BONANZA PIPING #2

project on the Twelve Mile River to supply power and water to the company's dredges and hydraulics. The ditch was 70.2 miles long and brought water from the Ogilvie Mountains through a conduit of ditch, flume (photograph 24), and inverted siphons (photograph 25) across the Klondike River at Bear Creek and up Bonanza Creek as far as Gold Hill, supplying water to all the hydraulics on the hills (photograph 26). The system consisted of 21 miles of flume, 37 miles of open ditch and 12 miles of pipe.[67] In the face of massive geographical and climatalogical challenges, the ditch was nonetheless built by the fall of 1909 to the mouth of Bonanza Creek. It took three summers, each approximately 120 days in length, to complete. In the spring of 1910, the company was able to turn the water on and start hydraulic mining on the lower Bonanza Hills, Crofton on the Klondike side, Lovett and Trail Hills on the Bonanza side.

Considerable trouble was encountered in that portion of the ditch that crossed areas of permafrost muck. Once the insulating moss covering was removed, the muck started to thaw in one area, and a section 200 feet by one quarter mile slid down into the ditch, making it necessary to construct fluming across this area. In the construction of flumes, the foundation beds were buried into the permafrost and quickly covered up with moss and brush to keep the muck from thawing. In some cases, a steam point was driven down through the moss to thaw a hole into which a pile was driven. This pile was left for a winter, allowing the pile to freeze in before the flume was constructed on it.

This water conduit system crossed ten valleys with inverted siphons, using California redwood stave pipe where the pressure was less

Inverted siphon, section of Yukon Ditch where it crosses the Klondike Valley at Bear Creek, using 14,759 feet of pipe to cross the valley.
YCGS DAMS #3

Inset: Upper Bonanza storage dam built to hold 43.6 million cubic feet of water, enough to last 40 days at the rate of 1.5 cubic feet per minute, used on Bunker Hill and Gold Hill, Bonanza Creek.
YCGS DAMS #15

than 200 pounds per square inch, and riveted steel pipe where the pressure was greater than 200 p.s.i. The largest of these siphons was the one that crossed the Klondike Valley at Bear Creek using 2,389 feet of wood stave pipe and 12,370 feet of steel pipe. The intake on the north side of the Klondike Valley was at 2,440 feet, and the discharge into the, ditch on the opposite side of the Klondike Valley was at 2,240 feet, a drop of 200 feet. The lowest point on the siphon on the Klondike Valley floor was 1,282 feet, 958 feet below the discharge. This gave a pressure of over 400 pounds p.s.i., so the line was built to withstand 500 pounds p.s.i.[68] In the Ogilvie Mountains, 7,300 miners inches of water were turned into the ditch; 2,300 M.I. were taken out at the 4.5–mile point and used to generate 1,650 electrical horsepower for the company's dredges. The other 5,000 M.I. were used on the hydraulic mining operations on Bonanza Creek. There was an elevation difference of 1,122.8 feet between the intake in the mountains and Gold Hill on Bonanza. The ditch system operated from the spring of 1910 to the fall of 1933.

Although the largest, this Yukon Ditch was not the only one. In 1905 there were 112 miles of ditch and fluming plus six inverted siphons and many miles of individual ditches from a half mile to ten or 12 miles in length.

Pumping

During the early part of the century, pumps were not very efficient at getting water to the miners on the benches. They were very large pieces of machinery, with at least two large wood–fired boilers which consumed large quantities of wood in order to maintain the necessary steam pressure.

When gold was found on the high benches, as much as 300 feet above the valley bottom, it was necessary to have a supply of water, there being little, if any, on the bench. The miners would build small reservoirs and ditches, collect what melting snow they could and hope for enough rain to keep them going. This amount of water only allowed them to mine with rockers, long toms or small sluice boxes. With the large number of miners working on the hills, it soon became apparent that some means of getting more water to these operations had to be

found. As a result, several pumping stations were constructed in an attempt to supply the miners—for a fee. As it turned out, the fee charged was so high that the miners could not afford it.

One such pumping unit was built by Big Alex McDonald at mouth of Adams Gulch on Bonanza; he was able to pump 100 miners inches to a height of 380 feet, supplying water to at least 15 claims.[69]

Messrs. Severance, Joy and Ashelby also had a pumping station on Bonanza, pumping water on to the second tier on Cheechaco Hill, where it also was used by 15 claims.[70]

Another pumping unit was set up on Bonanza by Messrs. Newman and Howard; it consisted of a triplex pump unit with eight by ten–inch water cylinders driven by an electric motor. The electricity was generated by steam–powered turbines.[71] This unit put 400 gallons per minute (38 miners inches) to the top of this hill.

William Northrop, on Oro Fino Hill, Bonanza, pumped his water from Bonanza Creek using a 40–H.P. boiler, a duplex piston pump with a 5.25–inch water cylinder, and an eight–inch steam cylinder pumping water through a 2.5–inch pipe to a storage reservoir on top of the hill, some 300 feet above Bonanza Creek. Here it was stored until needed.[72]

Another method collected seepage in a sump hole and used a small centrifugal pump, which pumped the water to the sluice box and returned it to the sump, after it had passed through settling boxes. After some use, the water became so thick the operation had to be shut down to allow the water to clear.[73]

Other pumping systems were used by the miners in the creeks, mostly to lift water a short distance from a sump where they were working, into a flume and then to the sluice box. The miners on the creek bottoms were faced with one of two problems: a) too much water in their mine pit or b) not enough water, in some cases, for sluicing purposes.

In the working areas, there was always a considerable amount of seepage water which was removed by hand pumps (photograph 15) or other methods. Chinese pumps were also used to keep cuts dry, but a Chinese pump needed 50 miners inches of water to make it work. It was powered by an overshot water wheel, which turned a conveyor belt system, on which there were containers that would pick up water from a sump and dump it where it would run away.

Another system used by the early bar miners who wanted to get water and who were mining a short distance away from the river was a water wheel. The water wheel was about 15 feet in diameter—much like a fish wheel—and it was placed on a float in the river, near the bank. Water containers of some kind were attached. As the river current turned the wheel, the buckets picked up the water and dumped it into a flume that led the water to the miner's operation. This would supply water for a small sluicing operation.

A large brush dam is in the foreground with several smaller ones back farther. These brush dams were used to hold tailings off the creek claims that were being worked below.
YCGC DAMS #17

Flumes were used to move water down the creek and keep it out of the work area. The branch line flumes coming off the main line are used to take water for sluicing.
YA #4518

From Riffle to Furnace

Whether in the form of gold dust or nuggets, placer gold is found in a crude state and has to pass through a refining process before it can be marketed. Such a process is not particularly elaborate, nor is it as expensive as that which base metals undergo, but it is essential. It is also potentially profitable to the assayer, usually a bank. Miners had to sell their gold to the bank at less than final value; they received the difference after the bank assayed the gold or heard from the mint to which it had sold the gold.[74] In effect, the miners "loaned" the assayer the difference between provisional and final payment, and paid charges to the bank for the service provided.

Klondike Currency

For a brief period in Yukon history, gold was more than a mere commodity; it was also a medium of exchange in the form of gold dust. Before the Klondike Gold Strike, it was valued as currency not only for its intrinsic worth, but also because there was more of it available than there was "hard" or "cheechako" money. Indeed, until the Canadian Bank of Commerce and the Bank of British North America brought their notes into the Yukon in May 1898, there was virtually no "hard" money, and what there was, was mostly American coins. "Trade" dust was valued at $17 an ounce, but its value could easily be debased by allowing it to get dirty. As a currency, such dust was potentially inflationary, so it was unpopular with the administration, which could not collect royalty on gold in circulation. On the other hand, its use in the Yukon as a medium of exchange did much to stimulate business there.

The government originally asked the Bank of Commerce to open a branch in Dawson, not only to act as its banker but also to facilitate the collection of royalties by purchasing gold.[75] In the process it would help replace gold dust with currency. The banks gradually reduced the

amount paid for dust, from $17 to $16 and finally to $14.50 an ounce.[76] From 1898 the administration, the two banks and the large companies in the territory worked to undermine the use of gold as a medium of exchange, finally succeeding in 1902. In that year, as part of a package of economic reforms which included the abolition of "royalties" and their replacement by an "export tax" on all gold shipped out, the government comptroller announced that, instead of royalties being paid in gold, the new export tax would have to be paid in currency, at the comptroller's office in Dawson. As the only places to obtain currency were the banks, the two branches became the crucial element in the elimination of gold dust as a currency and of the ambiguity that surrounded its dual use as currency and commodity. The action of the government and the banks was reinforced by Dawson merchants. The Dawson Board of Trade resolved that merchants would continue to accept gold in exchange for supplies, if such an agreement had already been arranged, but the 23% export tax would have to be added to the cost of the goods, in effect charging a premium upon the use of gold dust.[77]

When gold was used as currency, businesses had special weights used to weigh small amounts of gold. When the value of gold dust was reduced in May 1902, a jeweller put an ad in the *Sun*, stating that he had new scale weights of aluminum and German silver.

The merchants as well as the government and the banks were particularly anxious to reduce the value of gold dust and eliminate it as a currency. For one reason, gold varied in value from creek to creek and even on different parts of the creeks. Not surprisingly, miners took advantage of this fact by using the cheapest gold—occasionally adulterated by black sand—and using it to pay off for goods. Even when prices were adjusted to reflect this, a degree of uncertainty prevailed which merchants, government and the banks could not sustain.

Before the arrival of the Bank of Commerce and the Bank of British North America in the spring of 1898, the miners shipped their gold directly or via the trading companies to Seattle or San Francisco. There was no market in Canada for this commodity until a branch of the Royal Mint opened in 1907, so gold producers had to seek the best market available for the commodity. Once the Canadian banks opened branches in Dawson and began assaying gold there, they took over the functions of handling and shipping it.[79] They may have purchased a small amount themselves to back their note issues, but most was sent out to the United States.

Typical gold scale weights used by the traders in Dawson when gold was used as a medium of exchange. Some are for gold at $16 per ounce, some for gold at $15 per ounce. This style of weights was made by the Dawson jewelers.

J.A. GOULD

They never had a complete monopoly on assaying in Dawson but did most of it, because they offered other banking services both in Dawson and outside, and because the government insisted that miners submit their gold for the bank's valuation of it. The miner or his agent brought gold into the bank, occasionally as nuggets but more often in the form of dust with black sand, or as dry amalgam if mercury had already been utilized (see below). It was cleaned of visible impurities, then weighed in the presence of the vendor. Gold clerks developed the ability to distinguish between the gold produced on different creeks, so could estimate with some precision what its purity was. Once weighed, the gold was either purchased outright or the value estimated and an advance issued. The Dawson value was determined by deducting from the full assay value the government royalty, or after 1902, the 2.5% export tax (27.5 cents per average $15 ounce) and the bank's charge of 2% (26-28 cents per ounce). Final value depended upon the assay value determined outside.[80] From the 1930s, after the United States government raised the price of gold to $35 an ounce, the Dawson banks would advance $20 an ounce to

Determining Gold Values

The following table shows the value of gold in dollars from selected creeks between 1897 and 1916. The price of one ounce of pure gold was $20.67.

Creeks	1897	ca. 1903	1909	1916
Adams	—	—	—	12.71 – 16.43
Bear	15.00 – 16.00	15.00 – 16.00	—	13.31 – 14.86
Bonanza	15.75 – 18.50	15.75 – 16.50	15.54 – 16.84	16.12 – 16.97
Dominion	17.00	17.00	16.46 – 17.61	16.80 – 18.08
Eldorado	16.50	14.00 – 15.50	14.25 – 15.65	13.08 – 16.18
French	15.00 – 16.50	15.00 – 16.50	–	13.04 – 13.97
Gold Bottom	—	—	15.67 – 16.70	16.18 – 16.47
Hunker	17.50	12.50 – 17.50	15.36 – 17.23	15.50 – 16.90
Irish	—	—	—	12.89 – 15.33
Last Chance	—		13.85 – 15.57	14.09 – 16.49
Steep	—	—		19.24 – 19.49

the miner, and when the results returned from the mint in Ottawa, an adjustment was made. At $35 an ounce for pure gold, an ounce of Klondike gold was worth, on average, $25.

The basic assaying equipment was a melting furnace of fire brick, sufficiently hot to melt gold at 1063° centigrade and separate it from the silver and base metals alloyed with it. The dust was placed in the furnace, melted and the base metals drossed off. The molten gold was poured into molds, cooled and all remaining slag scraped off. The bar was then weighed, the difference between this and the original weight (about 1% or 2%) represented the loss in melting. Two chips were taken from the gold brick, one from the top and one from the bottom, at diagonally opposite corners. These chips were assayed for fineness. Pure gold ($20.67 an ounce) registered 1,000 fine. If the sample assayed at 800 fine, this would mean about 70 fine of dross and 130 fine of silver and would be worth $16.54 an ounce.[81]

Cleanups

When a miner is ready to clean up his sluice, he can do it in one of two ways. The riffles are lifted and washed; the gravel concentrates are then put through a long tom, shown in Figure 5, for further concentration. The cleanup can also be made in the sluice box itself. This is done by removing the riffles, washing them and setting them aside; then the gravel in the last six to ten feet of the sluice is shoveled to the upper end of the sluice. These riffles are then put back in the sluice box—this is a precaution against any gold being washed over during the clean up process. A small stream of water is turned into the sluice, enough to move the light gravels but not the gold. The miner then stirs the gravels with a shovel; this settles the gold to the bottom and allows the fine sand and gravel to wash out. Some of the coarse rocks and gravel are removed by hand using a rock fork. As the lighter sand and gravels wash away, the

Figure 5: Diagram of a typical long tom.

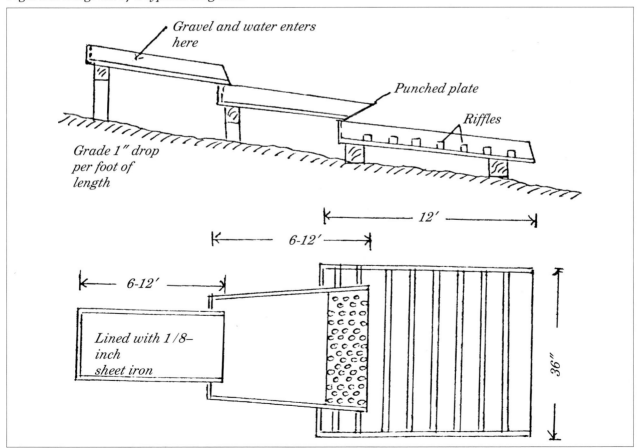

gold will appear at the upper end; this gold is swept into a pile with a whisk broom, picked up with a small scoop and put into a gold pan. After the sluice has been cleaned up, it is swept with a broom and all cracks and corners are brushed to recover any gold that may be there. The riffles can now be put back and sluicing can start again.

Once the gold has been removed from the sluice it is taken to the miner's home or in the case of a large operation or mining company, it would go to its gold room for further treatment. The type of treatment depends on whether mercury has been used in the saving of the gold or not. The treatment for mercury–coated gold, or "amalgam" as it is called, will be discussed later.

The cleanup, as it has been removed from the sluice box, has a lot of sand and other impurities mixed with it. As much of this as possible is removed by panning. The cleanup is then dried; the miner does this on top of his stove or in the oven, with not too much heat. Mining companies have a drying oven in their gold room for this purpose.

Cleaning Gold

Once dried, the gold is put through a set of screens where it is graded to three or four different sizes, making it easier to clean. The coarse material in the top screen can be cleaned by handpicking the bits of rock, etc., out of it. The gold in the lower screen takes more effort. A magnet is used to get any magnetic material out. The rest of the dirt is removed by blowing; a small amount is put in a wedge–shaped copper pan with the narrow end open. The person cleaning the gold shakes the copper blower pan from side to side, all the time while blowing on it. This moves the dirt to the narrow end, which is held shut with one hand. This dirt and sand is brushed out into a container, but is not yet thrown away, as there is always a small amount of gold in it that can be saved with mercury. Once the gold is thoroughly cleaned, it can either be sold in this loose form, or melted into bricks and then sold.

Amalgam

When mercury is used to save gold, the result is called amalgam. Most of the dirt that is

Blower pan, made of copper so that a magnet may be used to remove iron particles from the gold. It is about 12-16 inches long, eight to ten inches wide at its widest point, and three to four inches at the narrow end, with a depth of one to one and a half inches.
KNHS 33-9-6

in the amalgam can be removed by panning, or it can be put in a bucket of mercury and stirred; the dirt will come to the top where it can be skimmed off. This mercury–gold solution can be put in a chamois or moosehide bag, and the excess mercury can be squeezed off, forced through the seams of the bag. The remainder of the mercury can be driven off with heat in a retort, shown in Figure 6 below.

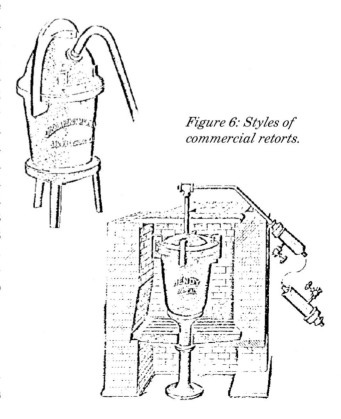

Figure 6: Styles of commercial retorts.

42

Retorting

There is a very simple method for getting the mercury off a small amount of gold—it is known as the "baked potato" method.[82] Cut a potato in half and scoop out enough to accept the gold amalgam. Put the amalgam in, and wire the two halves back together. Wrap the potato in several layers of aluminum foil to prevent the loss of mercury vapors and place it in an outdoor campfire to bake. (NEVER bake this potato in a house or cabin). After about 45 minutes, the mercury will have vaporized and saturated the potato, leaving the gold in the cavity. After removing the gold, crush the potato and pan it to recover the mercury. NEVER eat the potato! This method is fine for small amounts, perhaps up to one ounce; larger amounts need to be treated in a retort.

A retort is an iron pot–like receptacle with a lid from which a length of pipe protrudes. This length of pipe has a larger piece of pipe around it as a jacket through which water can flow. The inside of the retort is lined with chalk or a paste of finely ground fire clay; a paper bag can then be put into the retort and the gold amalgam into the bag. An asbestos gasket is put around the top of the retort, and then the lid put on and locked in place. The retort is put into a furnace— or in the case of a small retort, on a stand—and heat applied. The pipe from the top of the retort is led to a bucket of water as in Figure 7 below. The lower end, near the water, can have a piece of burlap attached which can hang in the water; this prevents any chance of water being sucked up into the retort should the heat fall, as water entering the retort could cause an explosion. Water is run through the water jacket, which cools the mercury vapors that come off the amalgam and condenses them back into a liquid which is trapped in the water. Mercury evaporates at about 357° centegrade. Gold will not melt until 1,063° centegrade has been reached. Heat has to be applied for about three hours to get all the mercury off the gold, and the fire should be kept constant all the time. The best type of furnace is one that is oil or kerosene–fired and gives constant heat. Retorting can be done with a wood fire, but it takes constant care and attention to maintain a good fire and vaporize all the mercury.[83] Once all the mercury is removed from the gold, the retort is allowed to cool, then opened and the gold sponge removed. One should be very careful not to breathe in any fumes from the retort as it is opened. The gold may be sold in this form or it may be melted down into bricks.

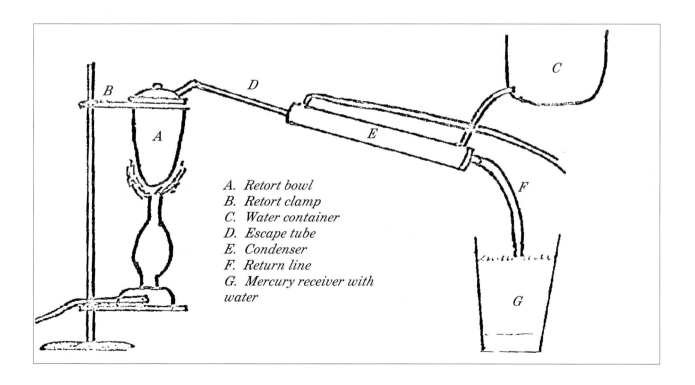

A. Retort bowl
B. Retort clamp
C. Water container
D. Escape tube
E. Condenser
F. Return line
G. Mercury receiver with water

Black Sand

All the sand that has been saved during the cleaning of the gold—this material is usually called "black sand" although there are much white sand and other materials in it—must be processed to recover what gold it contains. In the case of a mining company with gold room facilities, this black sand is put into a drum in which there are steel balls. A small amount of mercury is then added, plus water and some sodium cyanide or lye. The sodium or lye is to clean the gold so as to promote amalgamation of the gold and mercury. Enough heat is applied to keep the water very hot, and the drum is revolved for a number of hours. A door is opened in the drum and the contents run through a sluice where the gold amalgam is trapped in riffles or on a mercury–coated copper plate. This amalgam is treated as indicated above.[84]

Melting

Many of the larger operations melted their gold into bars before selling it to the banks, mainly because it was easier to handle, and being in bars, it was easier to keep track of. Crucibles in which gold is melted are made of a fine clay and graphite mixture. A new crucible should sit near the furnace for at least two melts before being used and then, when used, heated slowly. Once a crucible has been used, it is no longer necessary to take these precautions, but after five or six uses it should be discarded, for if one were to break during a melt, it could be very costly. Before placing the gold to be melted in the crucible, it should be cleaned and accurately weighed. In making a melt of 900 to 1,000 ounces, three–quarters of a pound of borax should first be melted in the crucible as a flux. The gold is then poured in, followed by one quarter pound of soda and a further one half pound of borax. The soda unites with the silica of any sand in the gold, and the borax unites with the iron content. If there are likely to be iron pyrites in the gold, a small quantity of scrap is added; in uniting with the sulphur, this forms an iron sulphide, which comes off in a slag. If no iron is added, a hard matter forms on the bullion bar, which is very difficult to remove. During the melt, the slag must be skimmed off a few times. A special long rod is used; it has an enlargement at the lower end to which the slag will stick. Once the rod becomes loaded with slag and heavy to handle, it is dipped in water and the slag broken off. A second flux of borax is added when this is melted; it is then ready to pour. The gold mold should be preheated to the point where oil will burn on contact before the gold is poured in.

When the gold has cooled in the mold, it is removed and placed in a bath of three or four parts of water and one part nitric acid to clean the gold of superficial deposits. The slag is then knocked off with a hammer, and the bar is brushed with a wire brush.[85]

Many of the large companies marked their bars with a number which was recorded against the weight of the bar, and in some cases, against the operation from which the gold came.

This Asahel Curtis photo shows miners working their cleanup.
PHPC

44

Gold Extraction

Thawing

Only in the Yukon, Alaska and Siberia were perpetually frozen gravels encountered in placer diggings. Not only was the pay gravel frozen solid year round, it was covered almost everywhere by a layer of vegetable mold—muck—from two feet to 100 feet thick, which was also frozen solid. All this had to be thawed before the gold–bearing gravels could be washed. Consequently, experience gained in the placer fields of California or British Columbia was of little use in the north.

The only thawed gravels were those along river bars, so it was here that initial prospecting was concentrated. From the river bars, prospectors were able to move out to river banks and bedrock outcroppings near the rivers, but in all cases prospecting was limited to the short summer season.

It was on the bars, first of the Stewart River, then of the Fortymile, that the first discoveries were made, but even here only surface "skim digging" was possible. In the summer permafrost prevented any but surface mining along the shore, and high water prevented bar mining until water levels dropped in late summer. In the winter, low water levels exposed large areas of the river bars, but the ground was frozen. Bar mining could only be undertaken efficiently between late summer low water levels during the brief period and freeze–up.

Efficient working of bars in the winter as well as mining in permafrost regions necessitated some form of thawing, either natural or artificial. Unless this could be done cheaply and efficiently, northern mining would remain impossible. A technology of thawing had to be developed in order to overcome the challenge of the permafrost, which locked placer gold into the gravels as totally as did quartz.[86]

Two thawing methods could be used: natural using solar heat, or artificial by the application of other types of heat. In order to use the sun's natural heat to thaw the ground in the summer, it was necessary to strip off the insulating cover of moss and brush. Once this was done, the sun would thaw the underlayer of

Sinking a new hole near Dawson in 1898.
PHPC

45

muck or gravel. Muck thaws very slowly, only three or four inches the first day, and then slower, unless the thawed material is removed as fast as it thaws. Should a miner be sinking a shaft, the sun's heat will only go so deep, until it ceases to have any effect on the frozen gravels. Also, unless precautions are taken, the sun will thaw the sides of the shaft near the top, causing the material to slough in. This creates a hazard for those working down in the shaft and, at the same time, makes the shaft larger at the top than necessary.

Fire Thawing

Until the late 1880s, no application of artificial heat was attempted, and only fine gold along river bars was mined. Coarse gold, however, which was more concentrated and richer, was mostly unavailable, because it was trapped in the permafrost. The working season was short, and therefore the amounts of gold taken from the Yukon were limited.

There are two accounts of the initial application—"discovery" would hardly be appropriate—of artificial heat to frozen gravels. Both agree on the date (1887) and the implications—year–round access to coarse gold and the consequent intensification of prospecting and mining activities. They differ, however, as to the motive and originator.

The first account was told by William Ogilvie. During the winter of 1887-88, he set up winter quarters near the Alaska–Yukon boundary. As the first and certainly the most accessible Canadian official most miners had dealt with, he was approached by them on legal and technical questions. He could give little satisfaction on the first, but he could on the second.

One important feature was brought forth at almost every meeting with anyone: the question of bedrock mining, as in more favoured regions farther south. The frost was considered by many an insuperable barrier and it was pretty generally believed that bedrock could not be reached by any practicable method. It was assumed that here, as elsewhere, the best pay would be found at lowest levels, but how to get through frozen sand, clay and gravel at reasonable expenditure of

time and money was the question, and as it developed, it was a burning question. As I had seen holes burnt in the frozen crusts of the streets in Ottawa to reach defective gas and water pipes, and I had several times had to use the process myself for other purposes, I suggested this, as I had seen it applied. As some of the miners had already used the firing method to secure the bar gravels uncovered by the very low water of the winter months, I used this as an argument in favour of burning down. Whether my advocacy had much, or little, or anything at all to do with the inception of the method I cannot say, but it was tried and a tremendous impetus was given to mining in the region. Bedrock was reached, and a quality and quantity of gold found that had not been dreamed of before.[87]

If this was applied technology, transferring a proven technique from one environment to another, similar one, the account in Adney of the initial application of artificial thawing at Fortymile more closely resembled serendipity.

Thawing the ground with fire had been thought of, but the idea was put to no practical use. Its possibilities were discovered in a curious way. At Franklin Gulch in 1887, Fred Hutchinson (now of 7 Eldorado) was following a pay streak which extended under water, and he was obliged to leave off work. That winter, however, after the ice had formed it occurred to him to chop the surface of the ice over the spot he wanted to work, but taking care not to break through. As the ice froze downwards, he kept on chopping, until he reached the bed of the stream, thus having built a sort of cofferdam of ice, which kept the water out of the hole. Hutchinson built a fire on the ground, and took out a little pay dirt. His neighbours observed his freakish undertaking and laughed at him. But the following year two of them made fires on the ground, and the diggings being shallow, took out considerable dirt. These first efforts were necessarily crude, but they demonstrated that ground might be worked which the sun's rays could not reach. In any event, it was a great leap forward, as twelve months' work was now possible instead of only two as before.[88]

There were, in fact, three methods of applying artificial heat: hot rocks, hot water and wood fires, all of which worked to some degree. Rocks were heated in a fire on the surface, then dropped into the shaft and covered; once they had done what little thawing they could, they had to be removed and then the thawed ground taken out. Hot water was no better than hot rocks, and it was more difficult to get the water out of the shaft; it was also a sloppy, muddy mess to work in. Wood fires proved to be the best method. The fires thawed deeper than either rocks or hot water and at the same time, dried out the gravels, making them easier to remove. Also, as most of the early mining was done during the winter, the gravels were dumped in a pile on the surface to wait for spring and water for sluicing, and did not freeze as hard, making it easier for the summer sun to thaw them prior to sluicing.

A dry wood fire would be built at the bottom of a shaft or at the end of a tunnel, then covered with sheet iron or, if no iron was available, with green wood. The fire was allowed to burn until all the wood was consumed, usually five to six hours. After waiting until the foul air was out of the shaft, the miner would go into it, remove all the thawed muck, then build another fire. One advantage of a wood fire was that it did not have to be watched. The miner could be doing other chores that were necessary, such as getting more wood or sinking a second shaft a short

distance away. In this manner, a shaft 20 feet deep could be dug in approximately 20 days.

The process of fire–thawing to bedrock was the first important adaptation of northern miners to permafrost conditions. It suited the needs of individual miners: no capital investment was needed, only the application of readily available hand labour and wood; it made possible the recovery of coarse gold from bedrock, thus increasing the volume of gold that could be removed; and it made possible—indeed it necessitated—year–round mining and consequent year–round habitation in the Yukon, creating the initial conditions for permanent white settlement.

Once the bedrock was reached, tunnelling or "drifting" became possible. Again this was apparently first done at Fortymile by O.C. Miller.[89] Such a method was expensive in terms of wood burned; according to A.N.C. Treadgold, it consumed over a cubic yard of wood for every cubic yard of gravel melted, but was inexpensive and technically easy in the absence of timber needed for the shafts.[90] Because the ground remained frozen during the winter, the shaft did not get too big. There was little danger of falling debris, and the cold air facilitated both the burning and the clearing of the hole. According to one source, Yukon miners in their unbraced shafts resorted to "coyoting"—a method of drifting outward into the pay streak with a series of radial tunnels.[91]

Thawing with wood fires underground.
J.A. GOULD

On Bonanza Creek, T.W. Allenby tried a novel way to thaw ground. He constructed a tank in which he built his wood fire and then, with the aid of a hand–operated blower and some method of leading the hot air down the shaft, he directed the air against the frozen gravels.[92] The item in the newspaper which reported Allenby's method did not describe how the hot air was led down the shaft, nor did it say how successful this method was.

Steam Thawing

Whatever may have been the advantages of fire thawing, it suffered from two serious disadvantages when used on the scale it was after 1896: it was labour intensive, and it consumed prodigious amounts of wood, which became scarcer and more expensive. Such an increasingly expensive, if effective, technology could not cope with the increased costs of working lower value ground after 1897.

Again through serendipity, or as a result of a conscious effort to reduce costs, the second contribution of northern experience to mining technology resulted to meet this need—steam thawing. Clarence Berry, one of the Klondike Kings, accidently found out how to use steam. He noticed that the steam escaping from one of his engines was thawing a hole in the nearby muck. He picked up the exhaust pipe, which was a rubber hose, and applying it to the frozen ground, he found he could thaw a hole in the muck the full length of the hose. He did some

experimenting, using whatever was handy to apply the steam to the frozen gravels, and found that a rifle barrel was best because it was strong enough to withstand the blows of the hammers needed to drive it into the gravel deposit. He drilled a hole in the side of the barrel near one end and attached a short pipe nipple for the hose connection. By plugging the barrel at the end near the hose connection, he could, by gently tapping the barrel, drive it into the gravel for its full length, and leaving it there he could thaw considerably more gravel, in a shorter time, than by using wood fires. It was also found to be safer to work in a shaft where steam was used, as there was no bad air or wood smoke to contend with. Heavy–walled iron pipe was soon used as a steam point, and eventually a solid head and a heavy point were added, making it easier to drive the pipe into the gravels.[93] This was a tremendous step forward in the thawing of the frozen gravel deposits; using steam points, the miners were able to thaw eight to ten feet per day, where as with wood fires they were only able to thaw two or three.

Steam as a means of thawing the pay gravels soon came into general use, and steam thawers were advertised in all Dawson papers and sold by merchants such as McLennan, McFeely and the "store that sells most everything," the Klondike Thawing Machine Co. Five cross heads (figure 9 at right) were used where more than one steam point was in use; usually there was a cross head for each four points. At first, wooden mallets made from nearby trees

A battery of eight steam points can be seen in this picture; two men have wooden mallets used to drive the points.
J.A. GOULD

A miner driving steam points underground. This is a photo of the first thawing maching underground on Gold Hill, 1900.
YA #1307

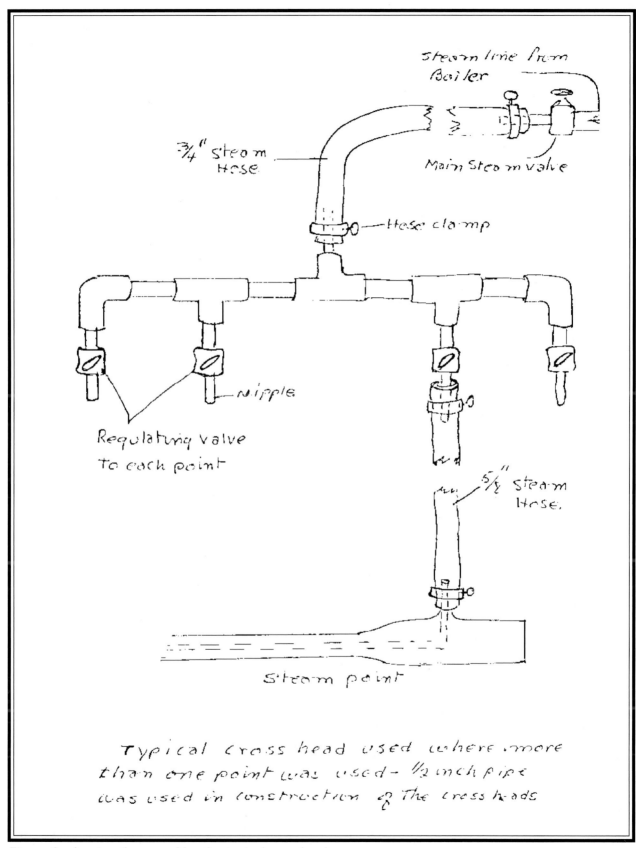

Figure 9, showing the assembly of a typical crosshead.

49

were used to drive the points, then the single jack hammer of the quartz miner was adopted, and later a double hand hammer of seven to 16 pounds was used. The heavy hammer was hard on the points and was only used where driving was extra hard; the ten–pound hammer size was the favorite. It was impossible to drive a point any faster than the ground could be thawed ahead of the point.

When driving points into the gravel, hot water was used instead of steam, the temperature of the water being 180-200°F. The flow of hot water through the point kept it from clogging as it was driven into the gravel deposit; once the point was in, the steam was turned on.

The eight–foot length of steam point was most commonly used. Shorter lengths did not thaw enough gravel to be economical, and longer lengths were cumbersome to handle, especially underground. Longer points, as much as 30 feet in length, were, however, used on the surface in front of dredges after dredging finally started.

In drifting operations, in underground tunnels, the points were driven into the gravel at or near bedrock, that being the easiest area for the point to enter. In easy ground one man known as the "pointman" could drive points and thaw enough ground to keep 16 shovellers busy. The usual practice was to have two men working together; one would drive and one would twist the point, making sure it was loose in the ground. They would change jobs every little while.

When starting a point, it was necessary to support it so that it was kept upright; this could be done with a stand or a box, or by the assistant. The point was very hot, so dry gunny sacks or similar material were used around the point as an insulator against the heat.

It was soon found that if steam was used when starting the points, all kinds of problems and hazards showed up. The steam filled the cavern making it hard to see. The point man had to bend down close to the point in order to see what he was doing. The live steam thawed the surrounding walls and roof, causing continual sloughing of rocks and gravels, and everything soon became soaking wet. Also, candles, the only source of light, flickered and had a tendency to go out. When miners started the points using hot water instead, these hazards were minimized.

Once the point was driven in to its full length, it was necessary to leave it to "sweat" for several hours and thaw the surrounding ground. Points were expensive, and in a large mine operation this sweating could tie up 50 or more points for several hours. Some inventive miner came up with the idea of using a smaller diameter pipe of the same length as the point, which became known as the "sweater." The steam point, which usually was of 5/8–inch diameter, was withdrawn and the smaller diameter 3/8–inch sweater inserted into the hole left by withdrawing the point. It would be left in to thaw the ground, making the point available to use elsewhere. The sweater, being smaller in diameter than the point, was loose in the hole, and this allowed the steam, which should be thawing the ground, to escape. To prevent this, narrow strips of gunny sack or jute were wrapped around the sweater back from the end. The sweater was then driven in, the jute being held in place by a caulking tool. Enough jute was used, so that the sweater was tight in the hole, keeping the steam from escaping.

Steam was distributed to the cross head and points or sweaters in such a way that they all had an equal amount of steam. There was a valve to each cross head and point for this purpose.

Once a set of points or sweaters was in place, it was necessary to inspect them from time to time to make sure they were working. If there was a reduction of steam pressure from the boiler for some reason, the point or sweater could fill up with water, cooling it off to the point where it was no longer effectively thawing the gravels. The point man soon became adept at reading the pulse of the point and knew when it was cooling or working properly.

The length of time necessary to thaw the gravels depended on the tightness of the gravel and the amount of clay in it. Normally eight–foot points or sweaters could be placed three feet apart in a five–foot thick pay streak and thaw inwards for a distance of nine feet in ten hours.[94] The amount of steam to run a point was found to be one to two horsepower with an average of 1.5 horsepower.

Another thawing method tried with some success was pumping warm water against the gravel surface. A sump was dug at the base of the shaft or near the face being worked, a pulsometer pump was set up and steam was led to the pump.[95] Water was pumped against the face, thawing and washing the gravel face down. The water would return to the sump; if the water in the sump cooled off too much, live steam would be injected into it. A large pulsometer pump could thaw as much as 60 cubic yards in a ten–hour shift. The average amount of gravel that could be thawed by a single steampoint in ten hours was 3.75 cubic yards; this was known as the "duty" of a point.[96]

The use of steam for thawing greatly increased production and, at the same time, reduced costs. It took a third less wood to thaw the same amount of yardage than wood fire thawing had taken. The introduction of steam for thawing also made it easier to mine during the summer months.

The boiler used for thawing could also be used to supply power for hoisting with larger buckets, thus increasing production as well as reducing costs. The miners found they could mine frozen ground cheaper than they could unfrozen ground with the underground methods. There was little or no costly timbering needed.

The cheapest method of thawing gravel was to let the sun do it, but in order for the summer sun to thaw the ground, it was first necessary to remove the insulating layer of brush and moss and then the muck that was on top of the pay gravels. The muck could be removed by hand— that is, it could be dug and wheeled away in wheelbarrows as fast as it thawed, or it could be washed away with water by turning the creek over it. Once the gravel was exposed to the sun, it would thaw at the rate of six to eight inches a day and could then be moved away until the pay gravels were reached. The gravels would be shoveled into the sluice box as fast as they thawed—this was the "open cut" method of mining.

Once dredging started in the Klondike, it was necessary to thaw the gravels in front of the dredges in large quantities in order for the dredge to have enough yardage to keep operating. Large steam plants were set up at each dredging operation with at least two 150–horsepower boilers and a large number of steam points. Two lengths of points were used. First, an eight–foot length called the "starter" would be put into the ground to its full length; it would then be pulled and a longer one inserted—up to

A small pulsometer pump of the type used to thaw ground and also for pumping water out of an area being worked. It operates on the principle of a heart, powered by steam.
KNHS MA.78.8.7

40 feet long, depending on the depth of the ground. The sequence of events for steam thawing in front of a dredge was as follows:[97]

1. Steam line boxes strung out
2. Gooseneck boxes and headers coupled on
3. Bar holes for starters put down
4. Starter point used to thaw first eight feet
5. Starter pulled and long point inserted
6. Point driven to bedrock
7. Points allowed to steam 12-48 hours
8. Points pulled, cleaned and straightened
9. Headers moved, starters put down; cycle starts over again to thaw a new section.

The steam pressure at the boiler had to be maintained at 100 pounds in order that there would be 25 pounds at the points. The steam lines were all strung out in insulated boxes (photograph 35) to minimize the heat loss, and each thawing operation at a dredge would have a large supply of wood on hand—3,000 to 4,000 cords. The cost of thawing in this manner was very high, almost 50% of the total operating cost, as the following table will show.[98] As can be seen in this table, the cost of thawing by steam was very high, but it came down slightly as better materials and equipment became available and efficiency increased.

Also, by the time the plants were set up, summer was usually well advanced, and the percentage that was thawed naturally could be as high as 44 percent and as little as seven, depending on the type of gravel deposit and the amount of muck overburden.

Year	CubicYds. Dredged	Total Cost of Dredging in Dollars	Total Cost Per Cu.Yd. in Cents	Total Cost Charged to Thawing in Dollars	Thawing Per Cu.Yd. in Cents	% of Thawing Costs of Total Cost Per CubicYd.
1909	2,381,880	760,742.25	31.94	368,024.42	15.45	48.37
1910	3,249,788	1,101,304.89	31.09	459,437.07	14.14	45.47
1911	4,151,249	1,470,674.76	35.43	731,309.14	17.62	49.72
1912	5,157,280	1,580,289.82	30.64	774,949.47	15.02	49.03
1913	5,133,575	1,575,872.20	29.53	696,526.71	13.57	45.94
1914	4,800,781	1,326,080.75	27.62	584,760.23	12.18	44.09

A field of steam points, thawing in front of No. 6 dredge. Two or three 150–horsepower boilers and thousands of cords of wood were used in steam thawing plants.
YCGC #3

Cold Water Thawing

The next step in thawing placer deposits for a large–scale operation—dredging in particular— was the cold water method. In this case the gravels to be thawed were close to 100% frozen. As knowledge and experience were gained in the use of the cold water method, an earlier start in the spring became possible.

The earliest cold water thawing was done by Edward E. Pearce and Ivor Johnson, who experimented for several years with different methods in Alaska. In one method they drilled holes, then inserted two and 1/2–inch pipe down which cold water was pumped. They thawed a shaft 30 feet deep in a very short time with this method in 1918. In the same year, they used forty 3/4–inch pipes which were driven into the ground and cold water pumped into them, successfully thawing a block of ground that they were able to dredge.[99] In 1919 their thawing plant consisted of a field of 100 points, which also worked well. They did not say how long it took them to thaw the ground, but it was 100% suitable for dredging. The cost of thawing the 12,000 cubic yards in this manner was 9.5 cents per cubic yard.

Their next experiment was with a seepage method. They blocked out a section of a creek 1,025 feet long by 60 feet wide and nine feet deep that they wanted thawed for dredging purposes. They dug ditches along both sides of this area,

A field of steam points thawing ground in front of dredge #5 on Bonanza Creek. Steam pipes were encased in sawdust–filled boxes to maintain the heat.
YCGC PHOTO #19

53

so that a portion of the creek water would flow along both sides. At a point about three–quarters of the way downstream, they sank a shaft down to and into bedrock. The top three feet of this area was already thawed naturally by the time they were set up, and this thawed area allowed seepage water to flow through and into the shaft. A pump of sufficient capacity was set up to pump out the water which flowed into the shaft, and this allowed the water to flow through the gravels between the two streams. The pump was installed on August 4, and by August 18 the entire block of ground was thawed. A total of 20,000 cubic yards was thawed in this manner at a cost of 1.25 cents per cubic yard. This was a tremendous saving over the steam method.[100]

The cold water thawing method was perfected in Alaska by the Fairbanks Exploration Company, a subsidiary of the United States Smelting, Refining and Mining Company. By 1924, cold water method of thawing for dredging operations was in general use.[101] This reduced costs for the large dredging company in the Dawson area, the Yukon Consolidated Gold Corporation, to as low as 4-6 cents per cubic yard. Y.C.G.C. records show the following change in costs. In the years 1920-22, 490,834 cubic yards were thawed with steam at a cost of 24.74 cents per cubic yard. In the years 1923-34, 14,024,568 cubic yards were thawed by the cold water methods at a cost of 5.06 cents per cubic yard. This was a saving of 19.68 cents.[102]

The Yukon Consolidated Gold Corporation set up large fields of points in units of 400-700 points per unit. In 1936 at their No. 5 dredge on Dominion Creek, they had a field of points numbering 8,199, made up of 11 units, each with 344-672 points. The pumps recirculated water at the rate of 6,000 U.S. gallons per minute against a 100–foot head, which gave a pressure at each point of approximately 20 pounds. The temperature of the water was never above 55°F. The thawing period was started on unit No. 11 on May 14 and was completed on unit No. 21 on September 13, thawing a total of 2,046,748 cubic yards which, after testing, was considered to be 100% thawed. The shallowest part to be thawed was 20 feet deep, the deepest was 34 feet. The cost of thawing this block of ground was only 2.48 cents per cubic yard.[103]

Once thawed, and without the insulating blanket of moss and muck, these gravels would stay thawed for several years, before the permafrost from below would freeze them back. The only problem—and this was a minor one—was the three to seven feet of winter frost which the dredge had to contend with each spring, but by mid or late June, this was usually gone.

Large winter dumps waiting for spring water to be sluiced.
YA #3933

54

Hand Mining

Placer mining is the only method used in the Klondike, although effort and money has been expended upon prospecting for lode ores in quartz. This section will concentrate upon placer mining, in which activity the author was active, both in hand and hydraulic methods, for over 30 years, working with his father and other old timers.

Some problems in placer gold mining are:

- Prospecting: i.e. locating a rich deposit, or at least one with enough gold to make working it worthwhile
- Ensuring an adequate supply of water
- Excavating, and in some cases elevating, the gold and gravel mixture to an adequate height for the water separation process to take place
- Bringing the gold, gravel, and water mixture together
- Separating the gold from the gravel and the other unwanted elements in the natural occurring mixture
- Removal of tailings and waste in such a way so as not to interfere with other claims or further mining

At the beginning of the Klondike Gold Rush, there were many harebrained schemes offered to the stampeders as gold–saving methods and devices guaranteed to win them fabulous riches from the gravels of the Klondike creeks and make them rich. Many of the stampeders of 1898 left Seattle, Vancouver and San Francisco with these devices; some arrived with them, but most left them along the way.[104]

Before the development of artificial means to thaw out the frozen overburden (after 1887), mining was possible only in the summer. Fire, and later steam thawing, made possible—indeed essential—winter mining, except for the washing of the gravels in the springtime, using the melting snow for sluice water. Depending just upon the results of winter drifting and adequate water supply for spring cleanup was a risky business, which might return a fortune, or turn up nothing.

Rather than take a chance on finding gold on an unprospected or an unproven creek, many of the miners would work for wages or take a lay on a claim or portion of a claim on a proven creek. In some cases, men were hired on the basis of "bedrock pay;" that is, they received no pay until gold had been taken out and a cleanup made. This was still being done by some of the small mining operations in the 1930s.

The early miners reckoned that in order to make their claims pay, they needed a four–cent prospect in thawed ground; this would yield $5.40 per cubic yard.[105] In frozen ground, they could make wages on a two–cent prospect, because timbering for the shafts and tunnels was unnecessary. One man could shovel and wash about five cubic yards of gravel in a ten–hour day. The rate of progress also depended on the type of gravel deposit, the depth of the pay gravels, and the availability of a good water supply.

To claim their treasures, the early pioneer miners employed most of the methods used in earlier gold fields of British Columbia and California. They also added a few technical refinements, fitting them to the special situations of the frozen north. The well tested gold pans, rockers, long toms, sluice boxes, arrastras, hand amalgamators and hydraulic equipment were used and adapted to the conditions in the north.

Gold Pan

Some variation on the gold pan has always been necessary for the final stages of separating gold from its surroundings, but the modern pan—which was as useful for frying eggs as washing out gold—was apparently not used by the Spanish or Mexicans. According to Rickard, it was introduced into California at the beginning of the Gold Rush by Isaac Humphreys, an experienced placer miner from Georgia.[106] For obvious reasons its use caught on quickly, and it became an essential tool for the prospectors and miners who moved out from California into the other western and northern gold fields,

The gold pan was the slowest method of processing gravels for their gold content, but it was,

Clarence Berry, one of the early claim stakers and eventually one of the richest miners in the area, is shown here on #6 Above, on Eldorado Creek, shoveling dirt into a lady's gold pan.
PHPC

and is, the most portable, and absolutely essential. Even in today's modern mining, it is almost indispensable, being used for sampling or prospecting ahead of the operation, checking to see that all the pay gravels have been put through the washing plant, and also for the cleanup. The gold pan is a metal dish, ten to 19 inches in diameter and three inches deep with sloping sides of approximately 40°. Sometimes the bottom of the pan is copper–clad to assist the use of mercury in the saving of fine gold. Very little water is needed in the operation of a gold pan; a full wash tub makes an excellent panning tub.

The pay gravels are put into the pan, one shovelful at a time. The pan is then immersed in water, and the gravels stirred by hand, making sure all lumps of clay and gravel are broken up. The pan is swirled in a circular motion to settle the gold to the bottom, then tipped away from the panner and lifted quickly out of the

water, causing some of the dirt to wash overboard; this is repeated two or three times. The pan then lowered into the water and shaken in a circular motion, again tipped forward, and lifted quickly out of the water. Any coarse materials have to be removed by hand, a step which ensures there is no silt or clay attached that might contain gold. Eventually, all the dirt will be washed away and, hopefully, only gold will be left. In this fashion, about a cubic yard of gravel can be processed in a day—a slow, tedious method to make a living. Even in the days of '98, when wages were $1 per hour, there would have to have been $10 worth of gold in every cubic yard to equal wages. Five cents to the pan would have yielded only $7.50 per cubic yard, so unless the pay gravels contained $10 or more to the cubic yard, some other method had to be found to mine the gravels.

56

Rockers and Long Tom

With the rocker, or cradle as it is sometimes called, or the long tom considerably more gravel can be washed than with the gold pan.[107] Very little water is needed when using the rocker; enough water can be carried in buckets from a nearby source if necessary. It is simply a box affair on rockers with gold–saving aprons inside, and a burlap or blanket mat on the bottom to save gold. The top portion of the rocker, called a sieve, is removable; it has a metal bottom punched with half–inch holes. Gravel is shoveled into this sieve; water is then either bailed in with a gallon can with a long wooden handle, or introduced by a hose. The rocker is rocked back and forth until the gravels are washed.

A rocker from the gold fields.
PHPC

A typical rocker operation during the early days of the Klondike. Some operations had as many as eight rockers working. One like this could probably wash 20–25 cubic yards in a ten–hour day.
YA #3928

57

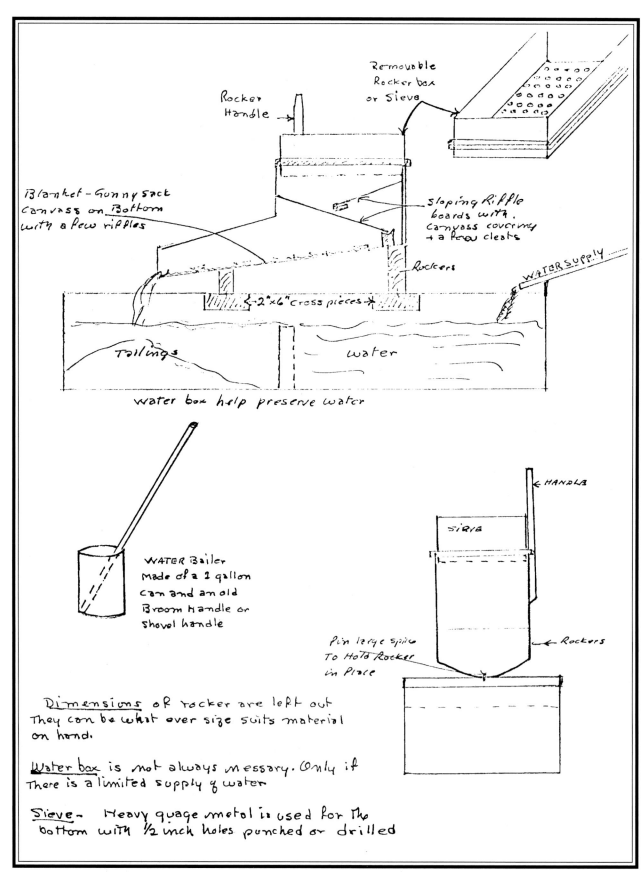

Figure 11, setup of typical rocker operation.

*Rupert's claim on
Cheechaco Hill opposite
No. 1 Bonanza.*
PHPC

Care must be taken not to use too much water
or shake the rocker too violently, as the gold
could be washed overboard. Where very little
water is available, a box can be built; this is considerably longer than the rocker, which sits on
top of it. It is divided in such a way that the
tailings from the rocker stay in one portion, from
which they can be cleaned out when necessary.
The water flows to the other section, usually at
the back of the rocker, and from there it can be
bailed while rocking (figure 11). Once the gravel
in the sieve is washed, it is thrown aside. More
gravel is then shoveled into the sieve, and the
operation is repeated.

*This Asahel Curtis photo
shows men using rockers
on Gold Hill. Rockers
were often used where
water was in short
supply.*
PHPC

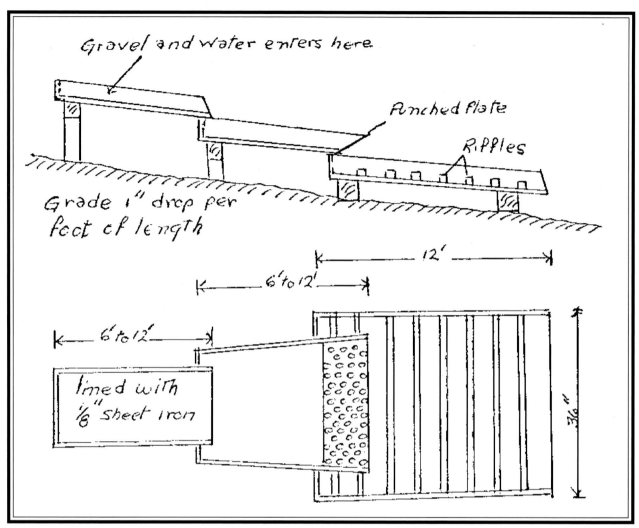

Figure 12, typical long tom construction.

The long tom is different. It is more like a sluice box, needs more water and is not rocked back and forth. Gravels are shoveled directly into the water, which can be flowing through the long tom or be bailed.[108] It is a rough trough, as much as 24 feet long, from 15-20 inches wide, with the lower end 30 inches wide. The whole thing is about eight inches deep. It is usually built in three sections, the first two sections being about six feet long, and the lower, wider section, which has the gold saving riffles, as much as 12 feet long. The top section, into which the gravel is shoveled, is lined with metal. The middle section, the lower end of which has half–inch holes in it, is also lined with metal. This section, known as a grizzle, is on a level plane while the rest of the long tom is on a grade of eight to 12 inches per 12 feet of length. The

water, gold and fines go through this grizzle and on to the riffles. The coarse material stops here and has to be shoveled off (see figure 12).

Sluice Boxes and Riffles

The sluice, or something very like it, has been central to placer mining since ancient times. Any water separation method demanded that the high specific gravity of gold be exploited; this was done, in different ways, by the German *buddle* and the Spanish *planilla*.[109] The former was smooth and took time to work properly, so was little favoured by California miners; the latter was closer to the sluice box.

Twelve feet was considered a sluice box length, so when the miners spoke of the grade or slope at which they set their boxes, it was for

60

the box length. A 12–inch grade equalled one inch for every foot of length. This system is still used by most miners today.

The early miners did not need a large sluice box for two reasons: not only did they lack large quantities of water, but they either had to shovel gravel into the box by hand or dump it in from a windlass bucket or wheelbarrow after most of the large rocks had been removed. The inside measurement of a sluice for hand mining was no more than 12 inches. The lumber used to construct the box was one inch by 12 inches by 12 feet long, and was planed on each side and edge. The sides had to fit tightly to the bottom because any crack or opening allowed the gold to fall through. The most common riffles used were poles cut from nearby wood. Poles roughly three inches in diameter by four to six feet in length (figure 13) were used and were held together in sections with a board either across the bottom

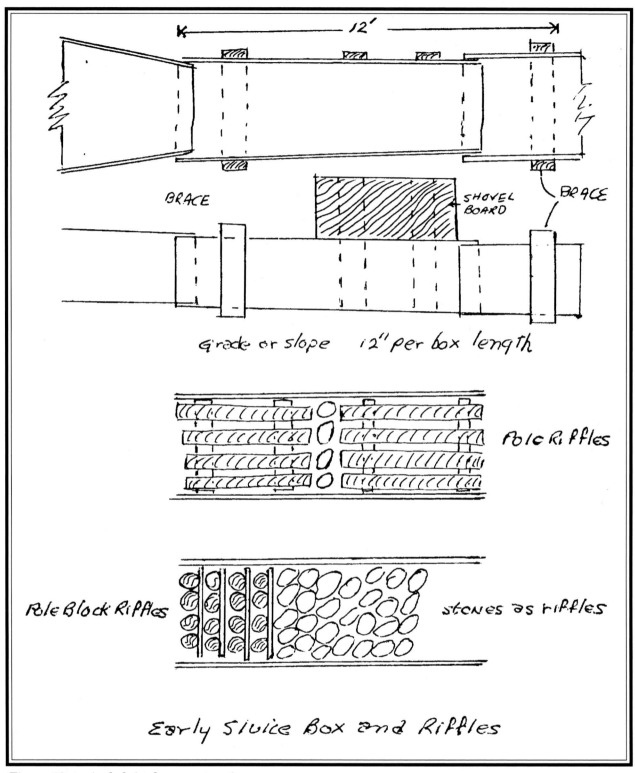

Figure 13, typical sluice box construction.

Sluice box in operation, showing water supply coming in at top, then the dump or mudbox, and then two lengths of sluice. The man at the dump box has a fork in his hand for removing rocks.
J.A. GOULD

near each end or across the ends. Other styles used blocks of wood cut from poles. These blocks were about six inches long and stood on end in the box; rocks were also used as riffles. Another board was nailed on the inside of the sides of the sluice. This board served two purposes: it held the riffles in place and kept the sides of the sluice box from wearing out. Early sluice boxes had enough taper in their length to fit inside the next box length. This style of box was not used when the large hydraulics started operating, as the slight taper in the box length acted as a restriction, slowing down the sluicing and often plugging the sluice, causing the gravels to run over the side. The sluice boxes for hydraulics were considerably wider and deeper, and each box length was tightly butted up to the next one.

Hand Mining

The depth of gravel and the availability of water dictated how the claim would be worked.

Bar mining was the first type of mining done in the north. With bar mining, there was always plenty of water, indeed too much if the low river bars were the ones to be mined. All that was necessary was to set up a rocker or sluice box, and start working. Once a sluice box was set up, water was turned in from the nearby creek or river in such a way that it could easily be turned out. The water was led to the sluice box with a ditch or flume that had a gate in it. This gate could be opened to allow water to go out of the flume and to be closed off from the sluice box. This gave the miner a chance to make a cleanup or make repairs to the riffles and sluice box. Also, it was not advisable to have water running through the box if no gravel was being washed, for it scoured the dirt and gold out of the riffles, washing them into the tailings, and losing the gold.

The first miners in the Yukon district did their mining during the summer months and in shallow ground, using only the sun's heat to thaw the ground. They would clear a section, possibly ten by 20 feet in size, of all brush and moss. They would then pick and shovel out the frozen muck. It was quicker to pick out frozen muck than to wait for it to thaw, as once the gravel was reached, the sun would thaw it at a rate of six to 14 inches a day. Once artificial thawing and drifting started, much more could be worked more quickly and efficiently.

Sinking a Shaft

The frozen conditions in the north were a boon as well as a hindrance to the prospector and miner. It slowed him down in digging, but it was not necessary to timber his shaft beyond the point that would thaw during the summer months. He started by clearing an area roughly three feet by five feet of the insulating layer of brush and moss for his shaft. He then picked his way down through the frozen muck to gravel. Once gravel was reached, it was necessary to thaw it, using hot water, hot rocks, or wood fires.

Wood fires were the best, at least until steam came into use in 1898. Fire would dry out the ground as well as thaw it, and ground thawed by fire did not refreeze as hard, making it easier to thaw for sluicing in the spring. Once underground mining became general, most of the mining was carried out during the winter months from November to March. Using wood fires, the prospector–miner was able to sink a 20–foot deep shaft in about 20 days. Once bedrock had been reached and enough gold found to justify a mine, the shaft was sunk a couple of feet into bedrock, and the miner then started drifting, following the pay streak. The usual way was to drift upstream. This way, any slight grade on the bedrock was advantageous in wheeling or moving gravel from the working face to the shaft for hoisting. It also kept any water that might be there away from the work area.

When sinking a shaft, a man can throw gravel out of a hole to a depth of approximately ten feet; after that, it is necessary to have some means of hoisting the gravels out. The earliest and simplest method of hoisting was the hand–operated windlass (figure 14). With this windlass, two men could hoist 100 buckets of the seven or eight–pan capacity per day (about 150 cubic feet of gravel.) Figure 15 shows a typical underground operation, with two men working underground and one man operating the windlass. The sump at the bottom of the shaft made it easier to dump the wheelbarrow full of dirt into the windlass bucket. Also, using two buckets—one going up full while an empty one came down—helped to speed things up. One man sinking a shaft and hoisting the gravels was a slow process, as he had to go down into the shaft, fill the bucket, climb out of the shaft and hoist the bucket.

One man, John Lundin, working on Quartz Creek in a 40–foot shaft, had his windlass rigged up so he could hoist as many as four buckets without climbing in and out of the shaft for each one.[110] He had enough rope on the windlass so that he could have a loop in the rope every 40 feet, the depth of the shaft. The pigtail hook that was normally on the windlass rope was fastened to the windlass bucket rope. He would fill the buckets in the shaft and fasten each one to a loop in the windlass rope, climb out of the shaft, and commence hoisting. When the first bucket arrived at the top of the shaft, the second one was ready to start up. He unhooked the first one and dumped it, then hoisted the second bucket, and the loops formed in the rope would

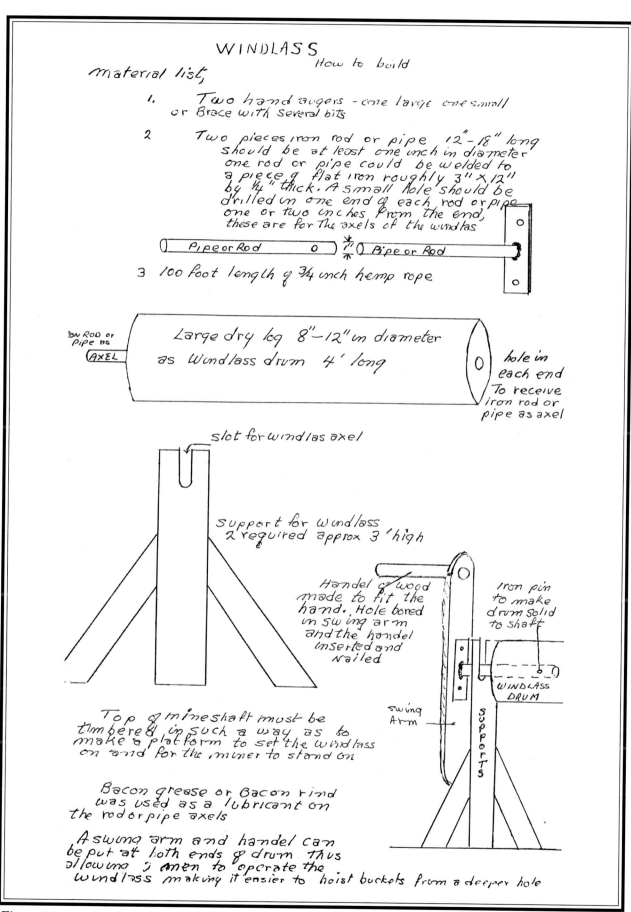

WINDLASS
How to build

material list,

1.   Two hand augers - one large one small
      or Brace with several bits

2   Two pieces iron rod or pipe 12"-18" long
      should be at least one inch in diameter
      one rod or pipe could be welded to
      a piece of flat iron roughly 3"x12"
      by ¼" thick. A small hole should be
      drilled in one end of each rod or pipe
      one or two inches from the end,
      these are for the axels of the windlas

Pipe or Rod   o   Pipe or Rod

3 100 foot length of ¾ inch hemp rope

ON ROD or
PIPE as

AXEL   Large dry log 8"-12" in diameter
              as Windlass drum 4' long

hole in
each end
To receive
iron rod or
pipe as axel

slot for windlass axel

support for windlass
2 required approx 3' high

Handel of wood
made to fit the
hand. Hole bored
in swing arm
and the handel
inserted and
Nailed

iron pin
to make
drum solid
to shaft

WINDLASS
DRUM

swing
Arm

SUPPORTS

Top of mineshaft must be
timbered in such a way as to
make a platform to set the windlass
on and for the miner to stand on

Bacon grease or Bacon rind
was used as a lubricant on
the rod or pipe axels

A swing arm and handel can
be put at both ends of drum thus
allowing 2 men to operate the
windlass making it easier to hoist buckets from a deeper hole

Figure 14, construction of a windlass.

Figure 15, primitive placer mining method of removing pay gravels with a windlass and bucket. The two men underground can handle ten to 12 cubic yards a day.

The hard work of bringing up the gold–laden gravel went on, regardless of the weather. The gold was there for those who wanted to work for it.
PHPC

wrap around the windlass, creating no problems in getting them out of the way. He continued in this manner until all the buckets were up and dumped.

Miners did not necessarily have wheelbarrows under ground; in many cases, the windlass bucket itself was used, either hauling it through the shaft on poles, or on a homemade cart, which rolled on pole rails. One man could probably hoist a windlass bucket from a depth of 50-60 feet.[111] Beyond that point, it became difficult. Counter weights could be added in the shape of buckets, probably filled with rocks, on the other end of the windlass from the crank

A windlass in operation on one of the claims on French Hill. The thawed pay dirt was hauled up the shaft by this simple but backbreaking machine and dumped until it could be washed through the sluice boxes in the spring.
PHPC

Underground mining; wheelbarrows are used to move the dirt to the windlass bucket at the bottom of the shaft. These are ten–pan size, side dump wheelbarrows, made in such a way that it is easier to dump them from the side.
J.A. GOULD

end; this would help with the hoisting. The fact that the ground was frozen and very little timbering was necessary helped the miners to excavate huge caverns underground. The gravels hoisted were dumped in a pile nearby; later on, when steam and self–dumps came into use, miners were able to dump further away.

Some miners set up their sluice boxes prior to hoisting pay dirt. They would cover them with boards or short poles and dump their gravels on this, being careful not to cover up either end of the sluice box. In the spring, when water was available for sluicing, it would be turned into the upper end of the sluice and the poles or boards covering the sluice would be removed one at a time, allowing the gravels to fall into the sluice and be washed. In this way, there was less shovel work.

The early miner had a unique way of determining or measuring the amount of gravel he handled in the course of the day, week, or whatever time period he wished. Alongside the shaft near the windlass was a peg-board with two pegs and two rows of ten holes. In one of the rows each hole represented one bucket. In the other row of holes, each hole represented ten buckets. As each bucket was brought up, a counter peg was moved to record it. The miners

Even dogs were used underground to reduce the burden on the miners.
YA #2185

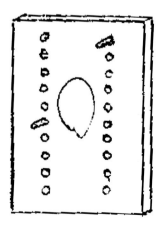

61 buckets

68

Skookum Jim's Claim No. 1, Above Bonanza. This claim proved quite valuable, as high as $300 to the pan being taken out.

PHPC

Windlass mining operation on Sulpher Creek. Buckets or large blocks of wood are used here as counterweights on the windlass to help with the hoisting.

YUKON TERRITORY, ITS HISTORY AND RESOURCES, *1909*.

Underground drifting, showing a pillar of gravel left to help hold up the roof. Also, after filling, the windlass bucket is hauled to the bottom of the shaft on a mine car.
J.A. GOULD

also had a table of measure to determine the number of cubic yards moved:[112]

Table of Measure

5.5 gold pans of gravel = one cubic foot
15 gold pans of gravel = one wheelbarrow
4 wheelbarrows = one self–dump bucket
10 wheelbarrows = one cubic yard
1 pan of gravel = 20 pounds
1 cubic yard = 3,000 pounds

With this table, the miners were able to determine the amount of gravel that was mined, whether they were hand mining or using self–dump equipment and steam.

Once steam was introduced for both thawing the gravels and hoisting, mining was carried on during the summer. This meant that the shafts had to be timbered in order to make them safe and to maintain their size. Shafts were timbered as they went down, using small logs or poles in most cases. In a few shafts, lumber was used, but very seldom. Moss was put around the outside of the timber, between it and the frozen sides of the shaft, as insulation against the steam heat and the summer heat.

Before the self–dump bucket, came into general use, buckets were hoisted, then swung from the top of the shaft on a boom either by hand or

using steam power. The contents were dumped on the pile of pay gravels or, in the case of a summer operation, into the sluice box.

One man's operation on American Gulch and Oro Fino Hill on Bonanza had a very large shaft, It was ten feet by 15 feet and was 90 feet deep. There was an elevator in each of the two compartments capable of carrying two loaded wheelbarrows. One side came up as the other went down with the empty wheelbarrow; it took 15 seconds to raise the loaded elevator. Power was obtained from a 35–horsepower boiler and a double drum hoisting engine. The mine had a record of hoisting 1,325 wheelbarrows of dirt in a ten–hour shift (approximately 130 cubic yards). The operator had a 5.25–inch duplex steam pump, powered by a 40–horsepower boiler, pumping water from Bonanza Creek through a 2.5–inch pipeline to a reservoir on the hill, for sluice water. In the spring of 1902, he had a dump 25 feet high by 200 feet long containing 80,000 wheelbarrows of pay gravels (8,000 cubic yards) ready for sluicing.[113]

With the advent of steam power and hoisting equipment, the miners worked out an efficient method of mining the deep gold deposits. They would sink a main shaft to bedrock and then into bedrock for a few feet; tunnels were then run up and downstream for a distance; if only one claim was being worked, then to the

n of an underground operation. spine stopeing
would start at far ends and work would progress towards
the main shaft.

D 19

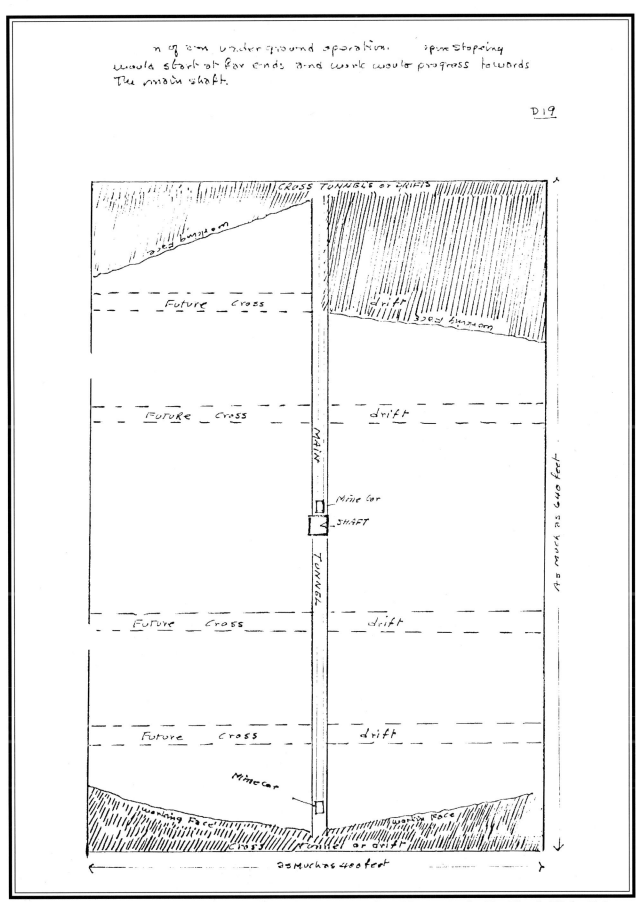

Figure 14, plans of an underground, hand mining operation from Mining in the Far North III *by T.A. Richard, 1909.*

Typical early day shaft timbering. This was uncovered on Bunker Creek by miner A. Kosuta in 1978. The shaft is 45 feet high and was probably sunk on this spot about 1900. The posts in the foreground were used to timer the drift. The windlass bucket and cart on page 27 came from here.

KNHS

Underground mining was hard, dirty work, but a few were rewarded with great wealth. These men appear to be mining the pay streak just above bedrock. Every inch had to be steam-thawed, mucked by hand, hauled up the shaft by windlass and piled until spring.

PHPC

limits of the claim. Cross tunnels were dug right and left at the ends of the main tunnel. These cross tunnels could be as much as 200 feet long, depending on the width of the pay gravels, but if the pay was wider than 400 feet, it would probably be better mined from another shaft and tunnel system. There is an economic limit as to how far the gravels can be transported. Mining was started at the far ends of the tunnels and of the cross drifts; everything would be mined out, taking about five to six feet of gravel plus a foot of bedrock. The miners would load a wheelbarrow at the face and trundle it to the main tunnel, where it would be dumped into a car with a six-wheelbarrow capacity. This would be run down the main tunnel on tracks to the sump at the foot of the shaft where it was put into a hoist bucket, and hoisted to the surface and dumped (figure 16). In one operation in Alaska, there were 22 men working underground, and each man had to make 100 trips with his wheelbarrow in a 10-hour shift.[114]

Thawing was done by steam. Steampoints would be put into the face at one end of the operation and allowed to sweat, while the miners took out the thawed gravels at the other end. Thawing had to be done with care to avoid melting too much ground or the cavern roof. Some protection for the miners was obtained by the

use of "stulls," with a head board placed at intervals in the cavern, and the miners worked as close as possible to the frozen face.[115] The ice seams in the gravel had a tendency to thaw, allowing large chunks of the roof to cave in. Gravel that is about to cave in dribbles quite a lot, and the stulls start cracking—this was the message to get out. If there was a cave–in, then the next cross drift was put into use. Once in a while a pillar would be left, usually at the junction of the main tunnel and a cross drift; this pillar helped to hold up the roof, and any waste and most of the rocks would be shoveled back into the worked–out area. In one case on Dominion Creek, a cavern 140 feet by 230 feet remained unbroken until mid–summer.[116]

Most of the deep ground was worked by this method. Shafts would be sunk where necessary, unless the mining was being done on a bench near the brow of the hill, in which case tunnels were driven in to the extent of the pay. In 1899 Harry Ash on King Solomon Hill on Bonanza drove five tunnels, each from 150-300 feet long, and then connected the tunnels with cross drifts every 25 feet. He started at the back and took everything out as he worked his way forward, working from all tunnels. He used 12 iron wheel mine cars which self–dumped into a steel–lined chute (325 feet long) leading to sluice boxes on Bonanza Creek, and had a 45–man crew working and two boilers for thawing.

Another operation on Cheechako Hill had two tunnels, each 350 feet long, connected at the back with a cross tunnel. The gravel was hauled out of the tunnel and dumped into a 500–foot bin at the brow of the hill. This bin was connected to another 500–cubic foot bin on Bonanza Creek with a 500–foot gravity car tram, and the gravel was then fed into a sluice box.[117] Yukon Gold Fields working on Cheechako Hill had the same type of operation.

Many of the miners used sluice boxes where there was sufficient water, but others used rockers. A man by the name of Andrews mining on Gold Hill used five rockers to wash as much as 450 12–pan buckets of gravel a day, which were

Pack train at Cheechako Hill. Notice rocker at right.

hoisted from his shaft. In August 1899 he cleaned up $1,000 a day by this method.[118] Thomas Nixon on a bench claim off Claim No. 2 on Skookum had 12 men working seven rockers, and he cleaned up as much as $1,000 a day.[119] All of these rockers were made in a manner similar to that shown in figure 11. There may have been a few differences such as more aprons, a longer bottom sluice with expanded metal over burlap or blanket, or small riffles, but they were essentially the same. A few of these rockers were made by tinsmiths in the Dawson tin shops; some even had coil springs on either side of the rockers to help with the rocking. Gravel that contained less than $3 worth of gold per cubic yard could not be mined profitably and, in many cases, even $5 a cubic yard was hardly enough.

Yukon Gold Fields, on Adams Hill, installed a number of jigs to wash the gravels from their mining operation.[120] Six jiggers were installed, capable of washing 15-20 cubic yards each per day. The gravel was carried from the tunnels by gravity cars, dumped into bins, then fed automatically to the jiggers. Coarse gravel, once washed, fell onto a conveyor which took it to the tailing pile. The finer material and water went into two lines of settling boxes; the water was then lifted back into tanks for reuse by means of a steam siphon. The sediment was shoveled onto the conveyor to go to the tailing pile. The water for this operation was brought up from Bonanza Creek to a tank tramway; each tank held 200 gallons and dumped automatically into a storage tank.

At least one miner tried sluicing all year round, although there is no indication as to how successful the experiment was. Mr. Stiles, mine superintendent for Big Alex McDonald, constructed a long, log building on claim No. 36 Above Discovery on Sulpher Creek. Inside the building were boilers for thawing and hoisting, sluice boxes, and large water tanks. Water was pumped from the mine to a feed tank for sluice water. Gravels were brought up and dumped into a chute that led to the sluice box. The gravel was then washed through the sluice onto a shaking grizzle, and the fines went into a settling tank. The coarse material was removed from the grizzle to the tailing pile by cars. Some of the water went to a receiving tank, and from there it was pumped back to the feed tank for reuse. Steam coils were placed in each water tank to keep the water from freezing, and a large fan was also used to move heat from around the boiler to the far end of the building. No mention of this operation was made in later publications, so there is no way of knowing how successful it was. It is possible that, being successful, the claim was worked out by 1902, when the next special edition of the *Dawson Daily News* came out.

In the spring of 1900 there were 5,280 men working on 560 claims; there were 155,080,180 pans of pay gravel on the dumps worth an average of ten cents a pan, or an estimated total value of $18,553,270. The largest dump was on Discovery, 1A and 1B Above Discovery on Bonanza, operated by George W. Carmack, the discoverer; he had 170 men working, and there were 4,000,000 pans of pay on the dump, worth $400,000. Thomas Lippy, on No. 16 Eldorado, had 60 men working with 3,000,000 pans of pay dirt on the dump, worth 15 cents a pan, for a total value of $450,000. One man, working alone on No. 3 Above Discovery on Sulpher hoisted 25,000 pans of dirt worth five cents a pan for a total of $1,250. As 25,000 pans equalled 3,600 windlass buckets, and this man had to thaw, shovel and hoist this material himself, he averaged probably 50 buckets a day for six months, or about three cubic yards of material per day.[122]

Open Cut Mining

As mentioned earlier, the open cut method of mining was used by the first miners in the north until 1887-88, when under ground mining got started.[123] When work began on Eldorado and Bonanza creeks in 1897, open cut became the method for mining shallow ground because it was cheaper and more efficient than drifting. Once the insulating layer of brush, moss and muck was removed, the sun would thaw the gravel six to ten inches a day.

To start, it was necessary to clear a piece of ground of all brush and moss; this was done by cutting, piling and burning.[124] Under the moss was a layer of frozen muck. The best way to get rid of this was to wash it off with water. When water from the creek was directed across it in channels, it soon washed deep trenches into the gravel, thus allowing the sun to thaw it rapidly. The water was kept directed against the mud banks, washing them down.

This method could be used when there were no other miners downstream from the claim being worked, or the downstream claim was owned by the same person. Otherwise, this layer of muck had to be picked up and shoveled into wheelbarrows and wheeled away, or if horses were available, a fresno or slusser scraper could be used. This overburden had to be put on a piece of ground that was either not going to be worked or had already been worked; otherwise, it would have to be moved again.

Creek water was another consideration. It had to be led around the area being worked, either in a ditch or by flumes. The miners along the creek cooperated to the point where there were miles of flume leading this water back and forth across the creek. Also, as the gravels in the creek thawed, water was produced which had to be kept out of the cuts, and this was done with hand–operated pumps or Chinese pumps. Once steam became available, steam–powered pumps were used.

When the muck had been removed, some of the gravel also had to be removed until the pay

Stripping muck off with the ground sluicing method. Creek water is directed against mud bands, and by keeping brush and solid materials clear of the mud, the water will soon strip the mud off.
J.A. GOULD

gravels were reached; these could be within four or five feet of bedrock. At this point, sluice boxes had to be set up; obviously this could not be done down in some of the cuts as there was no place for the sluice water or the tailings to escape. The sluice box was set up at creek level on posts and staging; this allowed the miner to lead water out of the ditch, through his sluice box for washing the gravels, and then across the cut. These long flumes were held in place with brac-

ing on either side. If the ground being worked was more than six or eight feet deep, the men shoveling could not shovel the dirt directly into the sluice box, which was above their heads. Staging was built five or six feet high; on this staging was a platform approximately four feet by eight feet in size; two platforms were sometimes necessary at different levels. One man would shovel from the pay gravel to the first platform, another man would shovel it from

Water diversion flumes, from which water was taken for sluicing purposes.
J.A. GOULD

76

there to the next platform, another would then shovel it up and into the sluice box. None of the large rocks were put through the sluice; sometimes they were used to build rock retaining walls, behind which would be thrown more rocks and whatever waste there was.

Besides men shoveling the dirt into the sluice, there had to be a man in the sluice to keep things running smoothly; he had a rock fork, and it was his job to fork all the rocks out as they were washed. At the tail end of the sluice, some method had to be used to keep the tailings from piling up. This meant at least one more man to keep it clear, or a horse–drawn scraper was used to move the tailings to one side. At this rate, it took up to five men to shovel and sluice one cubic yard of dirt; with wages at $1 per hour, it became rather expensive.

Once open cut work became general, it was found that a system other than the hand pump or Chinese pump was needed to drain the working area. In 1898, there was a movement on the creeks towards the construction of bedrock drains.[125] The first application for a bedrock flume drain was made by a miner on Hunker Creek during the summer of 1898. These drains had to be built with the cooperation of other claim owners, because they had to pass through their claims, but they were advantageous to the claim owners, who were then able to make use of the drain themselves.

Probably the longest one constructed was on Dominion Creek; it went from Claim No. 8 Above Upper Discovery to Claim No. 72 Below Lower Discovery, passing through 128 claims, for a total length of 12 miles.

This photo shows how winter dumps were piled on top of sluice boxes. The men at the two sluice lines to the right of the photo are sluicing the dump.
YCGC

Bedrock Drains

A bedrock drain is a method used to keep water out of the area being mined. Over 90% of modern placer mining operations use this method to keep the cuts free of water. All the creeks in the Klondike gold fields have a gradient steep enough that a bedrock drain can be constructed at a somewhat flatter grade and eventually reach bedrock. On some of the shorter creeks, bedrock can be reached with a drain in as little as 500 feet, depending on the depth of the ground; other creeks may require 3,000 or more feet of drain before reaching bedrock.

Modern drains are built with bulldozers or draglines and are merely open ditches, but the drains of the early days were covered flumes, all built by hand. A covered flume was constructed of lumber and set on posts until bedrock was reached, where it was then laid (figure 17). Using a covered drain and in an area that had already been worked out, the miner was able to dump his tailings and waste on top of the drain.[126] As work on the claim progressed upstream, the drain was extended upstream as well to keep the new working area dry.

The flumes that were used to keep the main creek water out of the working area (see bottom

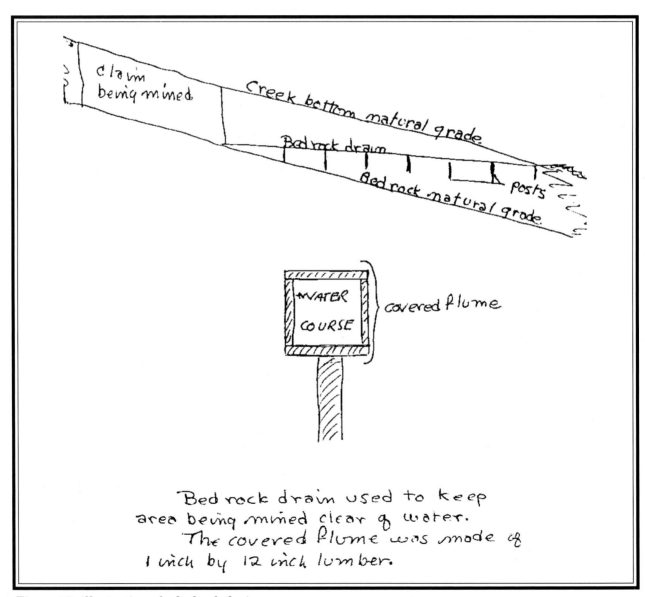

Figure 17, illustration of a bedrock drain.

78

photo, page 76) also provided a source of water for sluicing. The water was diverted by a gate and possibly a flume to the sluice box, where it was used and then directed back into the main flume. With all the miners along the creeks using this water and very little fresh water being added, the water quickly became very thick. This kind of water does not save all the gold, so some of it is washed over into the tailings. In some cases, "snipers" were able to make as much as $50 per day rocking the old tailings.[127] This thick water and the richness of the pay streak help explain why much of this ground could be worked several times. Bonanza Creek was mined by the underground method; it was then open cut; small dredges were later used; and from 1940 to 1959 the Yukon Consolidated Gold Corporation operated a large dredge on the creek.

Once steam power came into general use, open cut mining became a cheaper operation. It was no longer necessary to have men shoveling from one platform to the next in order to get the paydirt to the sluice box, as this was done by steam hoist. Large buckets or platforms, holding four or more wheelbarrows of dirt, were used to hoist the gravels either to the dump or, in the summer, directly to the sluice box.

Many operations used steam to hoist, but when it came to moving the hoisted material to the sluice box, horse or manpower was be used to swing and dump the bucket. The photograph below shows an open cut operation where wheelbarrows are used to load a wooden platform with sides on it, steam is used to hoist the platform, and a horse swings the boom to the sluice box where it is dumped by hand. In this operation, three platforms were used, so that hoisting was

Steam is used here to hoist a platform with three sides. One man holds a guide rope which is probably used to dump the pay gravels into the sluices. The platforms are loaded with wheelbarrows, and horses and scrapers are used for clearing the tailings and also for stripping off the overburden.
J.A. GOULD

Another view of several strings of sluice boxes, branching from the main water flume. One sluice is in operation, one is being dismantled to be moved and another is ready to be used.

ANITA JOHN COLLECTION #YT 233

a continuous operation. A horse and scraper were used to keep the tailings from the end of the sluice box. One platform can be seen hanging below the end of the boom; two or more are on the ground. The boom would be lowered with the empty platform that would be unhooked and another one hooked on and hoisted. One man can be seen holding a rope to steady the platform and keep it from dumping accidently; he, or one of the men at the sluice, may dump it.

Use of machinery increased very slowly in the Klondike gold fields, as R.G. McConnell reported in 1900.

The employment of machinery in the working of Klondike claims is gradually increasing, but is still insignificant—a fact due largely to the absence of roads and the consequent impossibility of transporting heavy pieces up the creeks. Steam thawers are largely used and steam pumps are gradually replacing hand pumps, Chinese pumps and water wheels for draining the pits. Steam hoists are used at a few mines but are not in general use. The greater part of the work at the camp is still done by hand, and this notwithstanding the fact that, taking into consideration the high price of labour, nowhere in the world could machinery be more profitably employed.[128]

As the miners became more experienced, they improved operations, so reducing costs and increasing the amount of yardage being worked. On the shallower creeks, and in areas where more than one claim was owned by a single miner, open bedrock drains were possible. Several long strings of sluice boxes and flumes would be used; the flumes would take water from the main water flume at the upper end of the claim. These flumes would lead the water to the sluice box that had been set up in the area being worked. As the ground was worked out at one sluice box, it would be shut down and the mining would move to the next sluice. The sluice that had been shut down would be cleaned up, dismantled, and moved up along the water flume to the next area to be mined. A number of the men would shovel the gravel into the sluice box, or in some cases, shovel from the gravel deposit to a platform, then into the sluice box. A horse and scraper were used to stack the tailings away from the end of the sluice box. When steam power and winches came into use, these handled the scrapers on the tailings.

Steam scrapers were also used to move the pay gravels into the sluice box. The first ones to use steam scrapers to scrape their dump into the sluice box were Kirkpatrick and Munroe on Hunker in 1902.[129] They were also the first to use self–dump machinery.

80

Self-Dump Mining

The introduction of artificial thawing and its refinement by means of first steam and then cold–water thawing represented major technological advances in reducing the costs of releasing gold from frozen gravels. Other costs remained, however, particularly those of labor and of supplies. To the extent that the cost of getting at the auriferous deposits could be reduced, to that extent more low grade gravels became reserves, operations were increased, and claims consolidated by a company, which could afford to employ capital intensive mining methods.

The use of the technologies of electricity, and particularly of steam, helped to mechanize Klondike mining to reduce costs. Steam could be used for thawing the ground; it could also be used as a power source, for hoists and scraper. Although gravels had still to be shoveled by hand into wheelbarrows and mine cars, larger volumes could be moved by machines than by men.

The self–dump machine was a Yukon–developed piece of mining technology, answering the need for a light, simple machine that could eliminate the labor intensive technology of wheelbarrows, by hoisting and conveying gravel from the bottom of a shaft or open cut to the dump or sluice box. It was similar in style to what was used in coal and iron mined, but it was altered for use in Yukon placer gold mining.[130] This important labor–saving device was invented in the Yukon by Bernard Esby, and as early as May 1902 self–dump equipment was in use on Kirkpatrick and Munroe's claim on Hunker creek. The machine had been manufactured in Dawson at McDonald's Mine works and was known as the "Dawson Carrier."[131]

The self–dump operated on a single 3/4–inch cable stretched between two posts, usually at an angle of 40˙, although it could work on less grade. One post, approximately five feet high, was situated near the shaft, or near the lowest area of an open cut. The other pole, called a "Gin Pole," was erected wherever the dirt was to be dumped. The carrier itself was worked by a single 3/8– or 1/2–inch cable. The hoisting cable extended from the drum of the engine to the top of the gin pole, where it passed through a block and extended to the carrier at the top of the shaft. The cable passed through a sheave in the carrier and down the shaft, passing through a block attached to the bale or handle of a bucket, and then returned to the carrier, where it fastened. When the signal was given, the cable wound around the drum of the hoisting engine, quickly lifting the bucket from the bottom of the shaft to the carrier where the handle of the block attached to the bucket bale lifted the hook in the center of the carrier, thereby releasing the sliding latch and automatically locking the hook and holding the bucket securely in the center of the carrier. The dumper was then pulled along the carrier cable to the point where the dirt was to be dumped. A chain was attached to the front side of the bucket, and at the end of the chain was a ring which passed along a cable, fastened a both ends and lying on the ground directly under the carrier cable. When the ring came in contact with a clamp which was fastened to the cable, the bucket was prevented from going any farther, and the strain on the chain overturned the bucket, dumping its contents. After dumping, the hoisting cable was slackened and the bucket and carrier slid back down the carrier cable until it reached the top of the shaft. An eccentric hook attacked to the sliding latch in the carrier then struck a ball fastened on the carrier cable. This action released the sliding latch, unhooked the hook, disconnected the handle of the bucket from the carrier, and allowed the bucket to travel back down the shaft.[132]

This self–dump equipment was used to hoist from shafts of underground mines and from open cut mines. During the winter, the pay gravel was dumped near the sluice box; during the summer sluicing season, it would be dumped on an apron of logs, and from there it would slide

Open cut, self–dump mining on Claim #8 Below discovery, bonanza Creek. A brush dam can be seen holding back tailings. On top of the dam are the sluice boxes and the pole apron on which the pay gravels are dumped from the bucket. The water supply flume runs across at the back of the photo.
YCGC

into the sluice box to be washed. It could also be dumped on a nearby pile, from where it could be shoveled or washed into the sluice box. The bucket would be filled in the pit or shaft with wheelbarrows.

This automatic dumping equipment enabled the mine operator to hoist an average of a bucket a minute, and some operators even claimed they could hoist as many as 750 buckets in a ten–hour shift—roughly 300 cubic yards of gravel.[133]

For summer sluicing operations, the sluice box has a sloping apron attached to one side of a series of small logs nailed tightly together. This apron had a slope of 40-50˙. The bucket of pay gravels would be dumped on this apron, and from there would trickle into the sluice. No large rocks would be hoisted from the shaft or pit as they were cleaned off and left on a waste pile. The sluice box and riffles were of the same size and style as used in hand mining.

This post card of a self dump mining operation on Dominion Creek dates from the turn of the century.
J.A. GOULD

Hydraulic Mining

Only the richest low–lying claims could be worked by hand, by shaft mining or by thawing. Auriferous deposits on the high benches could not be worked by any of these methods, but they could be worked if sufficient pressure were brought to bear on huge quantities of pay gravel so that the gold could be separated from the gravel. Hydraulic mining promised to do this. It was capital intensive and the per–ton cleanup was low, but it meant that huge tonnages could be handled at low cost because there was no need for elaborate machinery; water did all the work.

There may have been classical antecedents for this technology, but in its modern form hydraulic placer mining originated in California in 1853.[134] It continued in use there and was adapted elsewhere in the West. The first hydraulic mining operation in the north was on the Alaska side of Fortymile River, at the mouth of Franklin Gulch, where Frank Buteau and his partner P.G. McDonald set up a plant in 1892. They had to whipsaw 75,000 board feet of lumber for their sluice boxes and flumes. They also set up the first blacksmith shop, using a boulder for an anvil; the bellows for the forge were made of moose hide, which had been dipped in tallow to make it air tight. The Alaska Commercial Company brought in the hydraulic hose for them.[135] Whether hydraulic mining would work in the Klondike fields was uncertain for a time. Robert Anderson applied for a hydraulic lease in 1897 and acquired one by Order in Council in January 1898. There was bitter opposition to this, but Anderson's concession was never, in fact, worked.[136]

Besides the political opposition to the grouping of claims and to water concessions controlled by small groups operating with capital intensive methods, there were more practical questions about hydraulic placer mining. R.G. McConnell, writing in 1903, referred to hydraulic mining as being "still only in the experimental stage."[137] The year before, T.A.R. Purchas

had expressed the opinion that hydraulic mining on the high benches was not a viable proposition due to lack of water, frozen ground, too much barren overburden and no room in the valley for dumping tailings.[138] This was true then, but as time went on, methods were found to get water on the high benches and to contain the tailings; alternatively, the tailings could be dumped on claims which had already been mined out. By 1903 the major technical problems were overcome, and small hydraulic operations started.[139] In 1906 the Yukon Gold Company built a big dam on upper Bonanza and a ditch system that delivered water to Gold Hill for hydraulic purposes. That same year the company started construction of the Yukon Ditch, which would bring water, under pressure, from the Ogilvie Mountains to the hills on Bonanza Creek. This provided the large supply of water required for an economic hydraulic mine.[140]

Small–scale hydraulic miners who worked on the high benches constructed ditches around the hillside and collected water from melting snow and small streams. This water was stored in reservoirs near the area they were mining, and the pressure they had on bedrock depended on the depth of the ground. Pipelines were laid from the reservoir to bedrock, where they were washing the gravel banks down. Every 100 feet of fall on the water line gave roughly 44 pounds of pressure. A hydraulic giant or monitor (figure 20) was used to spray the water on the gravel bank, washing the gravel down and through a sluice box where the gold was caught.

Hydraulic mining with a gravity–powered water source became the cheapest method to mine gold. One hydraulic operation could mine ground that had as little as 14 cents worth of gold per cubic yard, at a cost of just under five cents per cubic yard.[141]

Sluice boxes were set in channels in the bedrock deep enough to get the proper grade. In some hydraulic operations on the high benches, the operator drove tunnels starting below the

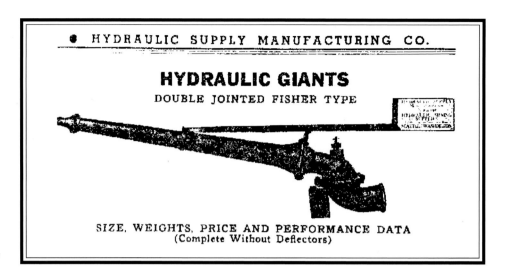

Figure 20, Hydraulic Giant or Monitor
(HYDRAULIC SUPPLY MANUFACTURING CO., SEATTLE, WASH., *CATALOGUE OF HYDRAULIC MINING EQUIPMENT,* SEATTLE, 1934, P. 38.)

brow of the hill; these tunnels were dug on hydraulic grade reaching the surface of the bedrock on the hill, well back from the brow of the hill, and sluice boxes were then put in. Due to the large volumes of gravel sluiced by these hydraulics, it was necessary to dig these tunnels on several of the hills, in order to get enough grade. A string of sluice boxes could extend from 100 feet to several hundred feet in length, the upper end of the sluice being kept as close as possible to the gravel bank that was being worked. As the gravel bank was washed down during the mining season, it moved away from the sluice boxes; the washed gravels ran through channels in the bedrock to the sluice boxes.

Hydraulic cut; this deep channel is cut in the bedrock in order to get sufficient grade on the sluice boxes, which can be seen in the bottom of the cut.
YCGC

84

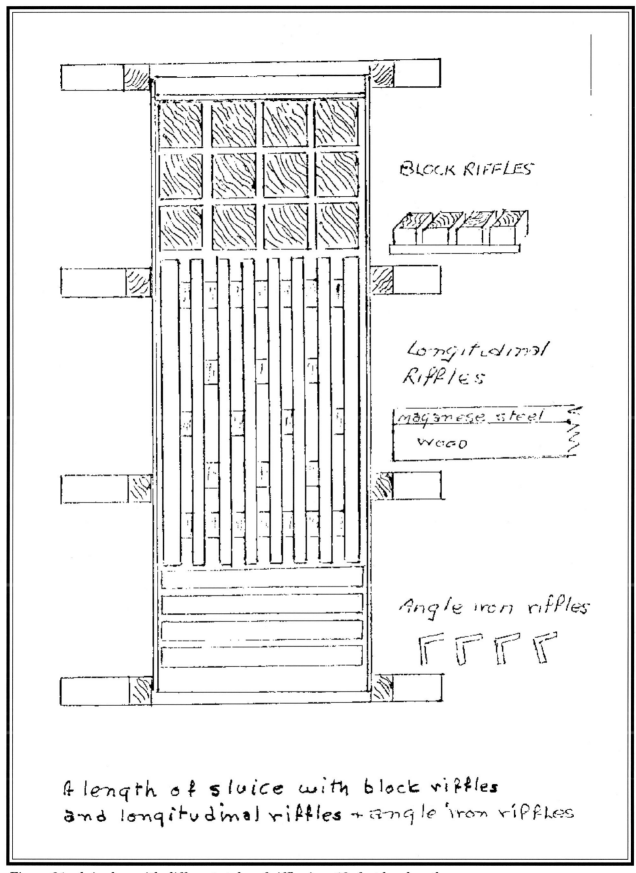

BLOCK RIFFLES

Longitudinal
Riffles

manganese steel
wood

Angle iron riffles

A length of sluice with block riffles
and longitudinal riffles + angle iron riffles

Figure 21, sluice box with different styles of riffles in a 12–foot box length.

*Hydraulic tunnel with
sluice boxes.*
YCGC

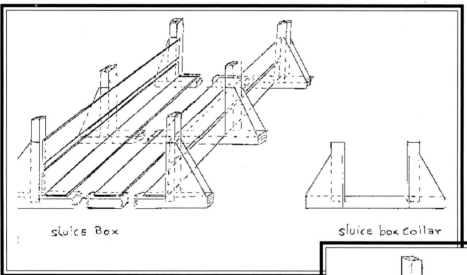

sluice Box   sluice box collar

Figure 22, construction of a sluice box.

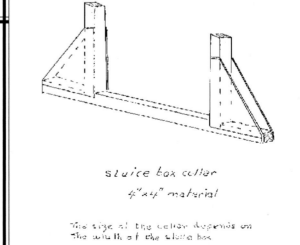

sluice box collar

4"x4" material

The size of the collar depends on
the width of the sluice box

*Figure 23, construction of
a sluice box collar.*

The sluice boxes for the large hydraulic operations were 30–48 inches wide and 24–30 inches deep. The amount of water used dictated the size of the sluice box. A 30–inch wide sluice would handle 200 to 300 miners inches of water. The early hydraulic miners liked to have water eight to ten inches deep in their sluice. The slope or grade used was eight inches to each 12 feet of box length—this was known as hydraulic grade.[142] Most small mining operations used 12 inches grade per box length.[143] Today's miners use a much steeper grade, as much as 24 inches, in most cases.

It was found that with a large volume of water and the eight–inch grade, riffles lasted a considerable length of time—possibly a full season of approximately 150 days. Three styles of riffles were used in the sluice boxes: block riffles, made of solid fir and usually ten by ten by ten inches; heavy angle iron riffles; or longitudinal riffles (figure 21).

Block riffles would be put in the sluice box in sections, the width of the sluice determining the number of blocks. They were held together with a one–inch piece of material nailed on one side, and the gap between the blocks was approximately one inch.

Longitudinal riffles were made up in sections to fit the width of the sluice. The material—two by six or two by eight lumber—stood on edge with a length of manganese steel of the same length and thickness on top. Each riffle was separated from the other by a spacer of the same width as the riffle.

Angle iron riffles were usually made up in sections, with several angles being welded together to make a section; or they could be set in frames that held them in the right position and the proper distance apart.

The sluice boxes used by the majority of hydraulic operators were of local spruce lumber. The sawmills of Dawson milled lumber they called sluice lumber, two–inch material planed on three sides. Miners made sure that all adjoining edges were planed and well fitted and that there were no cracks between the boards. All planed surfaces were on the inside. If rough lumber were used for the sluice box, it would be

A large brush dam is in the foreground with several smaller ones back farther. These brush dams were used to hold tailings off the creek claims that were being worked below.
YCGC

too difficult to make a good cleanup, as the gold stuck to the rough boards. There could be no cracks that would allow gold to fall through between the boards and be lost.

Figures 22 and 23 show the construction of a 12–foot length of sluice box and the collars, as used by the author and his father on their hydraulic operation on Hunker Creek. These boxes were easily taken apart when they had to be moved. The end collars were used in such a manner that the a next section of sluice box would fit into them.

Once mining started on the hills, a considerable amount of tailings came down into the valleys, which was acceptable if no one was mining there, but in many cases there was mining activity carried on in the valley. It was then necessary to keep tailings from being dumped on valley operations, and brush dams were built to hold the tailings back. These brush dams were made of small trees and brush, one layer being laid lengthwise, the next crosswise, and so on. In this manner, tailings were held on the hillside as high as 50 feet.

If a bedrock cut or channel where the sluice box was located had to be abandoned for any reason, or if it was necessary to add boxes to the upper end of the sluice, then a thorough cleaning of the bedrock was essential to recover any gold that had stopped there, and there was usually a considerable amount. First, all the gravel was sluiced out of the cut and through the sluice. Then men went in with picks, shovels and wheelbarrows, and starting at the upper end, one picked and shoveled forward to where another man shoveled gravel into a wheelbarrow and wheeled it down to near the sluice box. Once a day, a stream of water was turned on and the material dumped near the box was sluiced through the box. In this way, the bedrock was cleaned of all the gold, and at the same time, it was made ready so that more boxes could be added on. The upper end of the sluice was kept near the gravel bank. If the cut was to be abandoned once the bedrock and sluice box were cleaned up, the boxes would be removed to be used elsewhere. Some small operators, to ensure they got all the gold, used small scrapers and wire brushes; in this manner, they were able to recover every bit of gold lodged in the bedrock cracks.

An overall view of a hydraulic operation. Three monitors can be seen spraying water on the gravel banks. A long string of sluice boxes can also be seen.
YCGC

In Conclusion

It is hoped that the information in this report will be helpful to those using it as a reference. It is by no means a complete history on early Klondike mining. An attempt was made to touch briefly on many of the methods used by the early miners.

The methods used to mine gold during the early days in the Klondike were as basic as they are today. It was a matter of getting gold–bearing gravels and water together in the most efficient manner, so as to save the maximum amount of gold from each cubic yard of gravel as cheaply as possible. Today's mining methods and yesteryear's differ in that now high–powered machinery is used to move hundreds of cubic yards an hour. During the early days, only the pick, shovel and wheelbarrow were available to move the gravel, eventually producing some 50 million dollars worth of gold.

Many early stampeders came from walks of life far removed from placer gold mining and knew nothing about the methods used to recover gold. This did not deter them. Where possible, they used their previous experiences, adapting them to the job at hand, which sometimes resulted in odd ball methods and equipment, to say the least. Others staked claims and then leased them out to those who knew more about mining, in some cases making fortunes for both.

Wages were high for the time—$1.50 per hour—but they were still not enough for some workers. A certain amount of "high grading" went on. One '98er told of working on a claim on Eldorado where there was so much gold, it was easy to pick up an extra $30-50 a day. As they were going home after a full day's work, miners filled their pockets with gravel, panning it later on and realizing as much an additional $100. Another told of working an underground operation where he was getting paid only $1.00 an hour; the owner was getting rich, but workers wanted higher wages. When they approached the mine owner, he refused, saying, "Why should I pay you more money? You're down there where the gold is." The workers returned to work and began "high grading."

A typical windlass operation.
YA

Nomenclature

A/D – Above Discovery. Claims were numbered consecutively up or down stream from Discovery claim; i.e. 10 A/D is the tenth claim above discovery.

B/D – Below Discovery.

Bar Mining – Mining on the bars of rivers.

Cross Cut – A tunnel or drift leading off a main tunnel, usually at a right angle.

Clean Up – The act of removing the accumulation of gold from the sluice box. "The clean up" refers to the amount of gold removed during the clean up.

Drift – A horizontal underground passage, usually differing from a tunnel by opening onto a shaft and not necessarily onto the surface.

Drifting – The act of digging a drift.

Discovery – A find of gold or other mineral of economic value.

Discovery Claim – In the case of gold placer, the first claim stacked on a creek.

Gin Pole – A pole, 20 or more feet in height, usually at the point where material is to be dumped, serving as anchor for a cable used for a traveling hauling system—"self dump."

Miners Inch (M.I.) – The most common unit of measure determining water used or needed. First used in California in 1848, a miners inch was defined by California law as the flow of water through a one–inch square hole in a board during a 24–hour period with the top of the water on the supply side being six inches above the hole—1.5 cubic feet of water per minute. A simple method of measurement was to place a board in the stream with a weir cut in it large enough to allow the water to flow through. A stake was then driven into the quiet water behind the weir, the top of the stake being level with the weir. The amount water over the stake multiplied by the length of the weir determined the flow in miners inches; i.e. 5 inches of water over the stake multiplied by a ten–inch–long weir equals 50 M.I.

Placer – (From the Spanish *plaza* for place) A deposit of earth, sand or gravel, especially in a creek or river bed, containing valuable minerals; i.e. gold.

Placer Mining – A surface mining method applied to deposits of minerals accumulated into workable quantities of economic importance. Surface mining in some cases could include underground workings in a gravel deposit.

Pay Streak – That part of a gravel deposit that carries gold in large enough quantities to make it profitable to mine.

Prospecting – Searching for a mineral deposit.

A Prospect – A find of gold or other mineral worth further investigation.

Riffles – Devices used in a sluice to trap gold. Riffles can be made of angle iron, wooden poles or wooden blocks, positioned so as to allow gold to collect between them.

Right/Left Limit (RL/LL) – The right or left side of a valley when facing downstream.

Shaft – A vertical underground passage, at least three feet by five.

Sluice Box – A wood flume with riffles on the bottom through which gravel is washed to recover gold.

Sluicing – The act of washing gravel through a sluice box to separate gold from gravel.

Sluice Head – The amount of water used in sluicing. Each 50 M.I.s was considered a sluice head. One or more sluice heads could be required in sluicing operations. The Klondike miners usually bought water by the sluice head, paying as much as $4 per sluice head per hour.

Sniping – Superficial mining, usually with a rocker or long tom and a gold pan, for picking out spots of pay gravels that were missed when the claim was mined. Some early claim own ers allowed this type of mining on their claims; in return "snipers" would swear out affidavits of representation. In this way a claim owner kept his claim in good standing until he was ready to mine.

Stampede – A rush of people to a new discovery.

Stull – A post with a heavy board on top and braced against the roof of a cave, cavern or mine tunnel to support the roof.

Windlass – A wooden pole eight to ten inches in diameter and approximately ten feet long, with a hand crank on one or both ends, resting on a wooden frame over a shaft and used to hoist dirt from a shaft by means of a rope wrapped around the pole.

Windlass Bucket – A square wooden bucket of approximately 1.5 cubic feet capacity and used to hoist dirt from a shaft by means of a windlass.

Endnotes

[1] *Encyclopedia Britannica,* (1970), Vol, 10, p. 535, article on "Gold."

[2] For the early history of gold mining in the Yukon, see Allen A. Wright, *Prelude to Bonanza,* (Sidney, B.C.: Gray's Publishing Ltd., 1976), esp. chapter 5.

[3] Ray Vicker, *The Realms of Gold,* (New York: Scribner, 1975), p. 104. See also article in Encyclopedia Britannica, cited above.

[4] See Otis E. Young, *Western Mining,* (Norman, Okla: University of Oklahoma, 1978), esp. chapter I, pp. 3-32.

[5] Richard G. McConnell, "Report on the Yukon Gold Fields," *Geological Survey of Canada Annual Report,* Vol. 14, (1901), part B, pp. 68-69, in H.S, Bostock, *Yukon Territory: Selected Field Report of the Geological Survey of Canada, 1898-1933,* Memoir 284, Geological Survey of Canada, (Ottawa: Queen's Printer, 1957).

[6] Richard G. McConnell, Report on gold values in the Klondike high level gravels, *Report 979, Geological Survey of Canada,* (Ottawa, Queen's Printer, 1957), p. 217.

[7] McConnell, "Report on the Yukon Gold Fields," pp. 81-85.

[8] See Wright, *Op. cit.,* pp. 284-290.

[9] *Yukon Order of Pioneer Records.* The Nelsons and George Snow were charter members of the YOOP, Snow was chairman of the organizational meeting of the order held at Fortymile on 1 December 1894, and was later its historian.

[10] William Ogilvie, *Early Days on the Yukon,* (Ottawa: Thorburn and Abbott, 1913), p, 86.

[11] Capt. Henry Henderson, *The True Story of the Discovery of the Klondike by Bob Henderson,* (Edmonton: H.H. Hall CO., n.d.), p. 19.

[12] *Ibid.*

[13] Marguerite Carmack, *My Experience in the Yukon, Geo. W. Carmack,* n.p. (1933), p. 13.

[14] *Ibid.*

[15] *Klondike News,* 1 April 1898.

[16] C.A. Purington, *Methods and Costs of Gravel and Placer Mining in Alaska,* United States Geological Survey, No. 263, Washington, D.C. (1905), p. 43.

[17] *Dawson Daily News,* 27 July 1906, (hereafter cited *DDN*).

[18] Tappan Adney, *The Klondike Stampede,* (New York: Harper & Bros., 1900), pp. 249-252.

[19] *DDN,* 1 September 1899, Special Mining Issue.

[20] Harold Innis, "Settlement and the Mining Frontier, Vol. IX of W.A. Mackintosh and W.L.G. Joerg (eds.), *Canadian Frontiers of Settlement,* (Toronto: Macmillan, 1936), p. 206.

[21] Canada. Department of the Interior, *The Yukon Territory: Its History and Resources,* (Ottawa: The King's Printer, 1909), p. 93, (hereafter cited *Yukon Territory*).

[22] *Ibid.,* p. 95.

[23] *DDN,* 21 July 1909, article by A.J. Beaudette, Territorial Engineer, entitled "Evolution of Yukon Mining Methods."

[24] Thomas A. Rickard, "Mining Methods in the North," Part P IV, *Mining and Scientific Press,* Vol. 98, (1909), p. 590.

[25] Rickard, "Mining," Part I, Vol. 97, (1908), p. 589.

[26] *Yukon Territory,* 1909, p. 50.

[27] Purington, *Op. cit.,* p. 50.

[28] *DDN,* 27 July 1905.

[29] *Yukon Territory,* 1909, p. 48.

[30] DDN, 21 July 1909, Beaudette, "Evolution."

[31] Yukon Consolidated Gold Corporation, "Data and History a on Dredges and Hydraulics", n.p., (1942), p. 62.

[32] For the development of mining law, see Thomas A. II Rickard, *Man and Metals,* (New York: Arno, 1974), esp. V0L. II.

[33] I*bid.,* pp. 595-596.

[34] *Klondike Nugget,* 1 November 1899 (hereafter cited as *KN*).

[35] C.G. Motten, *Mexican Silver and the Enlightenment,* (New York: Octagon Press, 1972), p. 12.

[36] See Rickard, *Man,* pp. 621, 736; *KN,* 1 November 1899; W.P. Morrell, *The Gold Rushes,* (London: Dufour, 1968), p. 90.

[37] *Ibid.,* pp. 195, 379,

[38] *Ibid.,* pp. 124-127.

[39] Ogilvie, *Op. cit.,* p. 138.

[40] *Ibid.,* p. 139.

[41] Adney, *Op, cit.,* pp. 434-435.

[42] John W. Dafoe, *Clifford Sifton in Relation to his Times,* (Toronto: McMillan, 1931), pp. 153-155.

[43] Canada. Order in Council, No. 1189, 21 May 1897.

[44] Adney, *Op. cit.,* pp. 435-436. See also *KN,* 1 November 1899.

[45] See Lewis Green, *The Gold Hustlers,* (Anchorage: Alaska Northwest, 1977), esp. chapters 2-4.

[46] David R. Morrison, *The Politics of the Yukon Territory, 1898-1909,* (Toronto: University of Toronto, 1968), p. 74.

[47] Yukon Territory, 1909, pp. 72-73; *DDN,* 27 July 1905.

[48] Margaret Archibald, "Grubstake to Grocery Store: The Yukon Emporium, 1897-1907," *Canadian Historic Sites,* No. 26, (Ottawa: Parks Canada, 1981), pp. 135-136. For an "inside" list, see Adney, *Op. cit.,* pp. 465-466.

[49] *DDN,* Golden Clean Up Edition, 1902.

[50] An example of a homemade cart was located by Tony Kosuta, a miner on 80 pup Hunker Creek. Another example has been deposited in the Dawson Museum. See 1979 Creek Survey, photograph 13/17.

[51] See 1979 Creek Survey, photograph 17/3.

[52] *Ibid.,* photograph 10/20.

[53] See Purington, *Op. cit.,* p. 56, plate IVB. See also Young, *Op. cit.,* pp. 114-115

[54] *DDN,* 23 July 1906.

[55] *DDN,* 4 July 1906.

[56] *DDN,* 23 July 1906.

[57] *DDN,* 2 July 1906.

[58] *Yukon World,* June 1906.

[59] As told to the, author by his father, R.S. Gould, who mined on Hunker Creek from 1903 until 1958.

[60] Col. H.H. Norwood acquired the original rights in 1904, selling them soon afterwards to the yukon Gold Company. See *Canada. Department of the Interior, Report with Reference to the Yukon Territory,* by H.H, Rowatt, (Ottawa: King's printer, 1907), p. 6.

[61] This figure is cited by Innis, *Op. cit.,* p. 244. According to Rowatt, *Op. cit.,* (p. 6), the dam alone "cost about $200,000."

[62] See *Yukon Territory,* 1909, p.76; Green, pp. 96-97; Innis, *Op. cit.,* Pp. 244; Rowatt, *Op. cit.,* p. 6.

[63] Innis, *Op. cit.,* p. 245; *Yukon Territory,* 1909, *Op. cit.,* p.76.

[64] This section is based upon Green, *Op. cit.,* Chapters 2-4, and Morrison, *Op. cit.,* esp. Chapter 6,

[65] Purington, *Op. cit.,* p. 50.

[66] From article by Thomas A. Rickard, "The Yukon Ditch," probably in *Mining and Scientific Press,* Vol. 98, 1909. Supply for Yukon Gold

[67] From article by H.H. Hall, "Water Supply for Yukon Mines," probably in *Western Engineering,* August 1916; Innis *Op. cit.,* p. 244, gives slightly different figures: 19.6 miles of flumes, 38 miles of ditch, and 12.6 miles of pipe.

[68] Rickard, "Yukon Ditch."

[69] D*DN,* Golden Clean Up Edition, 1902.

[70] *KN,* 26 April 1900.

[71] *DDN,* Golden Clean Up Edition, 1902.

[72] *Ibid.*

[73] *Ibid.*

[74] See Victor Ross, *A History of the Canadian Bank of Commerce,* Vol. II, (Toronto: Oxford University, 1922), p. 159. Gold was purchased at $14 an ounce; the value of gold dust was considered to be $16 or $17 an ounce.

[75] Ross, *Op. cit.,* pp. 137-138.

[76] Ross, *Op. cit.,* p. 184; Adney, *Op. cit.,* p. 147; Innis, *Op. Cit.,* p. 205.

[77] *KN,* 1 May 1902; *Yukon Sun,* 26 April 1902 (hereafter cited *YS*).

[78] Adney, *Op. cit.,* p, 416, (1897); Innis, *Op. cit.,* pp. 204-205 (ca. 1903); *Yukon Territory,* 1909, p. 81 (1909); *Yukon Territory,* 1916, p. 31 (1916).

[79] See Ross, *Op. cit.,* Chapter 2, particularly pp. 162-166.

[80] *DDN,* 21 July 1909, article by F. Stanley Long (assayer at the Bank of British North America) entitled "Treatment and Marketing of Gold Dust."

[81] *Ibid.*

[82] Garnet Basque, *Gold Panners' Manual,* (Langley, B.C.: Stage Coach Publishing Co., 1974).

[83] Author's personal experience.

[84] Ernest Wolff, *Alaskan Handbook for Prospectors,* (Anchorage: University of Alaska, 1974), (2nd edition), p. 316.

[85] Purington, *Op. cit.,* p. 205.

[86] See Norman Ball, "The Development of Permafrost Thawing Techniques in the Placer Gold Fields of the Klondike," *Research Bulletin #25,* (Ottawa: Parks Canada, 1975).

[87] Ogilvie, *Op. cit.,* pp. 139-140. Somewhat more modestly, in his 1887 report, he referred to "a method lately adopted and which is called 'burning.'" Canada. Department of the Interior, *Information respecting the Yukon District,* (Ottawa: Queen's Printer, 1897), p, 42.

[88] Adney, *Op. cit.,* pp. 241-243.

[89] *Ibid.,* p. 243.

90 Ball, *Op. cit.,* p. 3. Adney, *Op. cit.,* p. 243, said that it took thirty cords of wood for a two–man, winter operation.

91 Young, *Op. cit.,* pp. 100-111.

92 *KN,* 1 November 1898.

93 Rickard, "Mining," Part I, Vol. 97, 1908, p. 812. Ogilvie (pp. 203-232) referred to "the miners" as the discoverers of this technique in 1897, an observation reinforced by the *DDN,* 6 August 1906, where mention was made of "... the men, ... who had for themselves invented and improved a practical thawing point...." See also J.B. Tyrrell "Development of Placer Gold Mining in the Klondike District," T*ransactions of the Institute of Mining Engineers,* 31, 1906, p, 561 for a third account of the origins of steam thawing.

94 From article by Hubert I. Ellis, "Thawing Methods at Fairbanks," probably in *Mining Journal,* 3 July 1915.

95 For the pulsometer pump, see Ball, *Op. cit.,* p. 5.

96 *Yukon Territory,* 1909, p. 88. Rickard, "Mining," Part I, p. 812, stated that the duty of a single point was from five to eight cubic yards in a 24 hour period.

97 O.B. Perry, "Development of Dredging in the Yukon Territory," *Transaction of the Canadian Mining Institute,* Vol. 18, 1915, p. 38.

98 *Ibid.,* p. 43.

99 Edward E. Pearce, "Cold Water Thawing of Frozen Gravel," Mining *and Scientific Press,* Vol. 124, 1922, p. 154. For a slightly different account, see Walter S. Weeks, "Thawing Frozen Ground with Cold Water," *Mining and Scientific Press,* Vol. 10, pp. 368-369.

100 Pearce, *Op. cit.,* pp. 154-155.

101 Yukon Consolidated Gold Corporation, *Operation of the Yukon Consolidated Gold Corporation,* Company Report, 1963 (by W.H.S. McFarland).

102 Yukon Consolidated Gold Corporation, *Record of Costs,* Company Report, 1942, p, 62.

103 Y.C.G.C., *Thawing Field Map,* 1936.

104 As told to the author by a '98er, Bill Strathie, who left Seattle with such a device, only to leave it in Juneau.

105 Rickard, "Mining," Part I, Vol. 97, p. 811.

106 Young, *Op. cit.,* p. 109, citing Rickard's *History of American Mining,* pp. 18-19. For the Spanish equivalent, the *batea,* see pp. 58-59.

107 For the origin of the rocker in California, see Young, *Op. Cit.,* pp. 110, 113-114.

108 *Ibid.,* pp. 116-118.

109 *Ibid.,* p. 58.

110 As told to the author by John Lundin, ca. 1952.

111 The author knew one man, George Crawley, a miner on Little Blanche creek (a tributary of Quartz) who hauled one hundred feet.

112 *Yukon Territory,* 1909, p. 81; author's recollection.

113 *DDN,* Golden Clean Up Edition, 1902.

114 From article by Rickard, "Mining," Part III, Vol. 98, I 1909.

115 For "stulls," see Young, *Op. cit.,* pp. 173-175.

116 McConnell, "Report," p. 103.

117 *DDN,* midsummer edition, September 1899.

118 As one bucket equaled one and a half cubic feet of gravel, these 450 buckets totaled 675 cu. ft. or 25 cu. yards. The $1,000 clean up thus equaled $40 for every cubic yard washed, or approximately 25 cents to a pan.

119 *DDN,* midsummer edition, September 1899.

[120] *YS,* 2 January 1900.

[121] *DDN,* midsummer edition, September 1899.

[122] *DDN,* 24 May 1900.

[123] Adney, *Op. cit.,* p. 241.

[124] Rickard, "Mining," Part II, Vol. 98, 1909, p. 88,

[125] *Ibid.*

[126] While mining on Eldorado creek in the 1950s, the author dug up several of these drains. He was informed of their use in conversation with old timers still living there.

[127] *DDN,* Golden Clean Up Edition, 1902.

[128] Richard G. McConnell, *Preliminary Report on the Klondike Gold Fields, Yukon District, Canada,* Report 687, Geological Survey of Canada, (Ottawa: Queen's Printer, 1900), p. 20. See also McConnell, "Report," pp. 103-105 for a later (1903) assessment of the use of machinery.

[129] *DDN,* 2 May 1902.

[130] *DDN,* 21 July 1909. See also Canada. Department of the Interior. "Appendix to the Report of the Superintendent of Mines, 1902" (Part IV, Annual Report, 1902). (Ottawa: King's Printer, 1902), pp. 10-15; and *Yukon Territory,* 1909, pp. 90-95.

[131] *DDN,* 2 May 1902.

[132] *Yukon Territory,* 1909, pp. 90-91.

[133] *DDN,* Golden Clean Up Edition, 1902.

[134] See Young, *Op. cit.,* pp. 125-131.

[135] *DDN,* Golden Clean Up Edition, 1902.

[136] Green, *Op. cit.,* esp. Chapter 2; Innis, pp. 226-229.

[137] McConnell, "Report," p. 104.

[138] *DDN,* 1 September 1899.

[139] In 1902-1903, the author's father worked for the Redmond Brothers who had a small hydraulic plant on Paradise Hill.

[140] See above, chapter 2.5.

[141] Yukon Consolidated Gold Corporation, *Records on Dredging and Hydraulics,* 1942, Annual Report.

[142] *Yukon Territory,* 1916, p. 124.

[143] Author's personal experience.

Bibliography

Adney, Tappen, *The Klondike Stampede,* New York: Harper & Bros., 1900.

Archibald, Margaret, ""Grubstake to Grocery Store: The Yukon Emporium, 1897-1907," Canadian Historic Sites, No. 26, Ottawa: Parks Canada, 1981.

Basque, Garnet, *Gold Panners' Manual,* Langley, B.C.: Stage Coach Publishing Co. 1974.

Bostock, H.A., Yukon Territory: Selected Field Reports of 1898-1953, Memoir 284, Geological Survey of Canada, Ottawa: Queen's Printer, 1957.

Canada. Department of the Interior. "Appendix to the Report of the Superintendent of Mines, 1902," (Part IV, Annual Report, 1902), Ottawa: King's Printer, 1903.

Canada. Department of the Interior. *Information respecting Yukon District,* Ottawa: Queen's Printer, 1897.

Canada. Department of the Interior. *Report with reference to the Yukon Territory* by H.H, Rowatt, Ottawa: King's Printer, 1907.

Canada. Department of the Interior. *The Yukon Territory. Its History and Resources,* Ottawa: King's Printer, I• editions in 1907, 1909, 1916, 1926.

Carmack, Marguerite, *My Experience in the Yukon Geo. W. Carmack,* n.p., I 1933.

Dafoe, John W., *Clifford Sifton in Relation to his Times,* Toronto: Macmillan, 1931.

Dawson Daily News, selected references, 1899-1954.

Ellis, Hubert I., "Thawing Methods at Fairbanks," *Mining Journal,* 3 July 1915.

Encyclopedia Britannica, (1970), Vol. 10, p. 535, article on "Gold."

Gould, John, Creek Survey, 1979, Unpublished report for Parks Canada, Dawson.

Green, Lewis, *The Gold Hustlers,* Anchorage: Alaska Northwest Pub. Co., 1977.

Hall, H.H., "Water Supply for Klondike Cold Mines," *Western Engineering,* August 1916.

Henderson, Capt. Henry, *The True Discovery of the Klondike by Bob Henderson,* Edmonton: H.H. Hall Publishing Co., n.d.

Hydraulic Supply Manufacturing Co., *Catalogue of Hydraulic Mining Equipment,* Seattle, 1934.

Innis, Harold A, "Settlement and the Mining Frontier," Vol. IX of W.A. MacIntosh and W.L.G. Joerg (eds.), *Canadian Frontiers of Settlement,* Toronto: Macmillan, 1936.

Joshua Hendy Machine Works, *Gold Mining Machinery Catalogue, #16,* San Francisco, 1905.

Keystone Drilling Catalogue, No. 2 - Fourth Edition, 1906, n.p.

Klondike News. 1 April 1898 (Only is One).

Klondike Nugget, selected references, 1898-1903.

McConnell, Richard George, *Preliminary Report on the Klondike Gold Fields, Yukon District, Canada,* Report 687, Geological Survey of Canada, Ottawa: Queen's Printer, 1900.

McConnell, Richard George, *Report of Gold Values in the Klondike High Level Gravels,* Report 979, Geological Survey of Canada, Ottawa: King's Printer, 1957, pp. 217-238, reprinted in Bostock.

McConnell, Richard George, "Report on the Yukon Gold Fields," *Geological Survey of Canada Annual Report,* Vol. 14, (1901), part B, pp. 64-113, reprinted in Bostock.

Morgan, Murray, *One Man's Gold Rush,* Seattle: University of Washington, 1962.

Morrell, W.P.I *The Gold Rushes,* London: 1940.

Morrison, David R.I *The Politics of the Yukon Territory, 1898-1909,* Toronto: University of Toronto, 1968.

Motten, C.G., Mexican Silver and the Enlightenment, New York: Octagon Press, 1972, p. 12.

Ogilvie, William, *Early Days on the Yukon,* Ottawa: Thornburn and Abbott, 1913.

Pearce, Edward E.I "Cold Water Thawing of Frozen Gravel," *Mining and Scientific Press,* Vol. 124, 1922, pp. 154-156.

Perry, O.B., "Development of Dredging in the Yukon Territory," *Transactions of the Canadian Mining Institute,* Vol. 18, 1915, pp. 26-44

Purington, C.A., *Methods and Costs of Gravel and Placer Mining in Alaska,* United States Geological Survey, No. 263, Washington, D.C.: 1905.

Rickard, Thomas A., *Man and Metals: A History of Mining in Relation to the Development of Civilization,* New York: Arno, 1974.

Rickard, Thomas A., "Mining Methods in the North," *Mining and Scientific Press,* Vol. 97, 1908, pp. 810-813; Vol. 98, 1909, pp. 86-89, 382-385, 587-591.

Rickard, Thomas A., "The Yukon Ditch," *Mining and Scientific Press,* Vol. 98, 1909, pp. 117-120, 148-152.

Ross, Victor, *A History of the Canadian Bank of Commerce, Vol.* II, Toronto: Oxford University, 1922.

Tyrrell, J.B., "Development of Placer Gold Mining in the Klondike District," *Transactions of Institute of Mining Engineers,* 31, 1906, pp. 556-574.

Vicker, Ray, *The Realms of Gold,* New York: Scribner, 1975.

Weeks, Walter S., "Thawing Frozen Ground with Cold Water," Mining and Scientific Press, Vol. 120, 1920, pp. 367-370.

Wolff, Ernest, *Alaskan Handbook for Prospectors,* Anchorage: University of Alaska, 1974, (2nd edition).

Wright, Allen A., *Prelude to Bonanza,* Sidney, B.C.: Gray's Publishing Ltd., 1976.

Young, Otis E., *Western Mining,* Norman, Okla: University of Oklahoma, 1978.

Yukon Consolidated Gold Corporation, *Data and History on Dredges and Hydraulics,* n.p., 1942, p. 62, Company Report, 1963.

"Yukon Order of Pioneer Records." Y.O.D.P., Dawson.

Yukon Sun, selected references, 1899-1904.

Yukon World, selected references, 1904-1909.

About the Author

Three Generations Have Mined the Same Ground
The Story of Nugget Hill
John Gould tells Family History

Robert S. Gould had left his home in the Musquobit Valley of Nova Scotia working his way west with the harvest when he heard of the gold strike in the Klondike. He did not have enough money to get an outfit to go north, so he worked in the coal mines of Washington state for awhile. Then in 1901 he came north. By the time he got to Skagway, the White Pass Railroad was in operation, so he did not have to hike over one of the passes. He and two other men from Nova Scotia—Harry Allen and George Allen, better known as "Daddy Allen" as he was the older of the two—landed in Dawson in either late May or early June 1901.

Dad immediately headed up Bonanza to Adams Hill where the Redmond Brothers, men from his hometown, were mining. He bought his first Free Miners Certificate at Grand Forks. He worked a short while on Adams Hill and then moved over to Paradise Hill on Hunker Creek where the Redmonds also had a mining operation. He staked his first claim on Paradise Hill, where he found it too deep for hand mining for the amount of gold that was there.

While working for Charles Redmond he had an accident in which he broke a couple of ribs. While mending he went across Hester Creek to Nugget Hill, did some prospecting and staked a claim. The Goulds were an independent family, farmers in Nova Scotia, who always preferred to be working for themselves. So when Dad staked this claim on Nugget Hill he thought, "Now I have a job."

During the first few years on Nugget Hill he had three partners, James W. Murphy and Mary Jane Murphy both from his home in Nova Scotia and a man named Charles Reed. Dad eventually bought out his partners. Mary Jane Murphy died in February 1913 and it wasn't long afterwards that J.W. Murphy decided to take his family back to Nova Scotia. He was the last partner to be bought out in 1918.

James W. Murphy had a blacksmith shop at Grand Forks for a short time which he sold to his partner. The Murphy family then moved on to Nugget Hill in 1905. Dad had built himself a small cabin which he moved out of so the Murphy family of seven could move in. He then had to build another one for himself.

Murphy ended up moving into Dawson where he and Dad opened a blacksmith shop on Third Avenue.

My father Bob Gould met his wife-to-be, Mabel Stacey, nee Whitehead, when she came from Boston, Massachusetts, in 1917 to visit her sister Margaret (Mrs. Angus Chisholm), who was a friend of Bob Gould. They were married in 1918 and went to live on Nugget Hill where they raised a family of five boys and a girl.

Dad, being a farmer from Nova Scotia, made sure there was a good garden, a green house, a milk cow, chickens and pigs, so we were self–sufficient. We had our own butter, milk, eggs, bacon, fresh vegetables, etc. There was also root house for storage in the basement of the small cabin.

After he bought out his partners, Dad hired three to four men in the spring of the year when there was plenty of water and maybe kept one man on during the rest of the summer, but water for mining on Nugget Hill was a problem. Like many farmers if there was no rain there was no crop. It was the same with mining, no water meant no gold.

However, we did fine and were never in want. We had no idea what the depression of the hungry 1930s was about. In 1932, Roosevelt put the price of gold up to $35 from $20. This was a shot in the arm to the gold mining industry of the Klondike—the dredging companies as well as the small miner.

99

It wasn't all work. Time was taken to pack a picnic lunch and go fishing for a mess of fresh grayling for the dinner table. On August 17 we would head for Dawson for the Discovery Day celebration. Of course if it rained, Dad would have to work and we knew that, but we hoped for good weather anyhow, and it usually was nice. When the blueberries were ripe we went out picking, some of mother's friends from around the creek and from town would also come to pick. Fresh blueberry pie was a great treat.

Dad and Mother had a windup record player, one of those Edison types, the kind that played the cylinder records. Friends from down in the valley would come up on Nugget Hill for an evening of entertainment; life on the hill was good.

Our father had bought some property in Burnaby, British Columbia, many years earlier and in the fall of 1933 we moved out, taking the last boat on October 10. Dad went back north every April to mine and came back to the Burnaby family home in the fall. I went to school in Burnaby for a few years but in the spring of 1936, I went back to Nugget Hill and worked with Dad every summer until the war came along.

Every miner had to be a "jack of all trades.' We had to know how to use a forge, which was needed to keep drills and picks sharp. Every miner had a forge, and some welding was done in the forge as well.

Every summer when the spring run off water was done we were out working on the ditch to keep it in shape. Whenever a heavy cloud bank would come up over the hill in the direction of our water source, Dad would go out where he could watch to see if it was raining. One time I asked him why he watched and his answer was, "I'm sky mining."

A trip to town 16 miles away for entertainment or supplies was an all day trip by horse and buggy.

In 1942, I joined the Canadian Air Force and went overseas as a pilot. During my training in Ontario, I met a girl whom I married when I came back from overseas in October 1945. I brought her to Dawson and the cabin on Nugget Hill in 1946, the same cabin that my father had brought his bride to 27 years earlier.

When Madelaine arrived in Dawson "City," she expected a large place with street cars, etc. She did not expect to see tumbled-down buildings or stores that when you walked in you either went down hill or up hill, depending on which way the permafrost had twisted.

I continued to work with Dad until 1958 when he finally retired at the age of 80 after working 55 years on Nugget Hill. I worked with Dad every year except for the 13 that I spent working for Klondike National Historic sites. Even in those years, I did some work on the claims.

Dad said he came north to make a stake and go back onto the prairie wheat farming. In 1914 he had come close to selling out to the Yukon Gold Co., but the First World War came along and stopped the sale.

When the price of gold was allowed to find its true value and started to go up dramatically, I knew I had to get back to mining full-time. So in 1980 at age 60, I retired from K.N.H.S. and went back to full-time mining. My son Peter started to work with me. We bought pumps, a loader, a bulldozer, a trommel washing plant and a welder.

Up to this time the mining on Nugget Hill was pretty well a hand operation. Dad and Murphy built two-and-a-half miles of ditch to bring water from a nearby stream to the reservoir on top of the hill. Hydraulic monitors were used to wash the gravel banks down and through the sluice boxes where the gold was saved. Wheelbarrows, picks and shovels were used extensively and eight pound sledge hammers were used to break up the bigger rocks so they would wash away. Large boulders were broken up with dynamite.

Peter continued to mine with some help from me until 1998. The third generation Gould gold miner on Nugget Hill, 96 years after the first Gould staked a claim on the hill.

Robert S. "Bob" Gould at the monitor. John Gould on D4 dozer, Nugget Hill, 1948

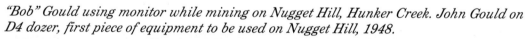

"Bob" Gould using monitor while mining on Nugget Hill, Hunker Creek. John Gould on D4 dozer, first piece of equipment to be used on Nugget Hill, 1948.

5870
" A Dump."
Mining Scene
in the Klondyke.

Postcard Views of Klondike Mining

CONSTRUCTING WOOD STAVE PIPE, YUKON GOLD CO.

PUBLISHED BY LANDAHL'S EMPORIUM, DAWSON, Y. T.

No. 810.—Construction of the Twelve Mile Pipe Line, Y.T.

No. 808.—Hydraulicking on French Hill, Y.T.

5872
"A Self Dumper."
Improved Hoisting
Method. A Yukon
Mining Scene.

5869
A Mining Scene
in the Klondyke
Gold Fields.

ALL PHPC

103

Early Mining Stock Certificates

BOB MAJNI

KLONDIKE

Cigar box label.
BOB MANI

1898 BY AMERICAN LITHOGRAPHIC CO. N.Y.

106